TestSMART

for Language Arts—Grade 6

Help for
Basic Language Arts Skills
State Competency Tests
Achievement Tests

by

Rachel Still

ecs

ECS TestSMART™ Basic Skill-Building Lessons Software with Management System, Grades 1-10

Quality, cost-effective, sequential skill-builders for learners of all ability levels

	Number of Lessons	License for 1-5 CPUs	License for 6-15 CPUs	License for 16-24 CPUs	License for 25-up CPUs
Level 1-6 Reading	324	ECS2185-05	ECS2185-15	ECS2185-24	ECS2185
Level 1 Reading	54	ECS2045-05	ECS2045-15	ECS2045-24	ECS2045
Level 2 Reading	51	ECS2061-05	ECS2061-15	ECS2061-24	ECS2061
Level 3 Reading	54	ECS2088-05	ECS2088-15	ECS2088-24	ECS2088
Level 4 Reading	60	ECS210X-05	ECS210X-15	ECS210X-24	ECS210X
Level 5 Reading	58	ECS2126-05	ECS2126-15	ECS2126-24	ECS2126
Level 6 Reading	47	ECS2142-05	ECS2142-15	ECS2142-24	ECS2142
Level 7-10 Reading	81	ECS2169-05	ECS2169-15	ECS2169-24	ECS2169
Level 1-6 Math	172	ECS2193-05	ECS2193-15	ECS2193-24	ECS2193
Level 1 Math	17	ECS2053-05	ECS2053-15	ECS2053-24	ECS2053
Level 2 Math	33	ECS207X-05	ECS207X-15	ECS207X-24	ECS207X
Level 3 Math	24	ECS2096-05	ECS2096-15	ECS2096-24	ECS2096
Level 4 Math	35	ECS2118-05	ECS2118-15	ECS2118-24	ECS2118
Level 5 Math	24	ECS2134-05	ECS2134-15	ECS2134-24	ECS2134
Level 6 Math	39	ECS2150-05	ECS2150-15	ECS2150-24	ECS2150
Level 7-10 Math	68	ECS2177-05	ECS2177-15	ECS2177-24	ECS2177
Level 1-6 Reading & Math	496	ECS2207-05	ECS2207-15	ECS2207-24	ECS2207
Level 7-10 Reading & Math	149	ECS2215-05	ECS2215-15	ECS2215-24	ECS2215
All Levels Reading & Math	645	ECS2223-05	ECS2223-15	ECS2223-24	ECS2223

TestSMART™ Interactive Lessons, Grades 1-10

Great resource for improving test scores. Lessons cover all the IRA and NCTE standards.

	Number of Lessons	License for 1-10 CPUs	License for 11-24 CPUs	License for 25-up CPUs
Level 1-10 Reading/Lang. Arts	1145	ECSIL-10	ECSIL-24	ECSIL
Level 1 Reading/Lang. Arts	140	ECSIL1-10	ECSIL1-24	ECSIL1
Level 2 Reading/Lang. Arts	170	ECSIL2-10	ECSIL2-24	ECSIL2
Level 3 Reading/Lang. Arts	190	ECSIL3-10	ECSIL3-24	ECSIL3
Level 4 Reading/Lang. Arts	170	ECSIL4-10	ECSIL4-24	ECSIL4
Level 5 Reading/Lang. Arts	145	ECSIL5-10	ECSIL5-24	ECSIL5
Level 6 Reading/Lang. Arts	160	ECSIL6-10	ECSIL6-24	ECSIL6
Level 7-10 Reading/Lang. Arts	170	ECSIL7-10	ECSIL7-24	ECSIL7

To order, visit www.educyberstor.com or contact ECS Learning Systems, P.O. Box 791439, San Antonio, TX 78279.

Editor: Lori Mammen **Page Layout & Graphics:** Jayme Salinas **Cover Design:** Educational Media Services

ISBN 1–57022–361–0

Printed in the United States of America.

Contents

Notes

Welcome to *TestSMART*™!!
It's just the tool you need to help students review
important language arts skills and prepare for
standardized language arts tests!

Introduction

During the past several years, an increasing number of American students have faced some form of state-mandated competency testing in English Language Arts/Writing. Some states use established competency tests, such as the Iowa Test of Basic Skills (ITBS), to assess student achievement. Other states focus on the skills and knowledge of their particular curriculum. For example, Texas has administered some type of competency test since 1980.

While some of the language arts tests are multiple-choice tests, many states also require students at varying grade levels to write compositions. These states include Texas, New York, Kansas, Ohio, Florida, California, North Carolina, Indiana, and Arizona, to name a few.

Whatever the testing route, one point is very clear: the trend toward more and more competency testing is widespread. By the fall of 2001, at least 48 states had adopted some type of English language arts assessment for students at various grade levels. In some states, these tests are "high-stakes" and determine whether or not a student is promoted.

The emphasis on competency tests has grown directly from the national push for higher educational standards and accountability. Under increasing pressure from political leaders, business people, and the general public, policymakers have turned to testing as the primary way to measure and improve student performance. Although experienced educators know that such test results can reveal only a small part of a much broader educational picture, state-mandated competency tests have gained a strong

foothold. Teachers must find effective ways to help their students prepare for these tests—and this is where *TestSMART*™ plays an important role.

What's inside this book?

Designed to help students review and practice important language arts and test-taking skills, *TestSMART*™ includes reproducible practice exercises in the following areas—

- sentence structure
- spelling
- capitalization
- punctuation
- grammar
- usage

In addition, each *TestSMART*™ book includes—

- a master skills list based on language arts standards of several states
- teaching strategies
- complete answer keys for multiple-choice questions
- descriptions of writing tasks and the attributes of successful compositions
- prompts for various types of writing
- scoring rubrics for assessing student writing
- checklists for student writers
- a reproducible answer sheet

5

The content of each section of *TestSMART*™ is outlined below.

Sentence Structure: This section of *TestSMART*™ includes 18 practice exercises with questions that focus on—

- recognizing compound/complex sentences

- demonstrating knowledge of sentence combining

- recognizing run-on sentences

- recognizing sentence fragments

- identifying complete and correctly written sentences

- identifying correctly edited sentences

Standard Usage: This section of *TestSMART*™ includes 33 practice exercises with questions that focus on—

- spelling (e.g., frequently misspelled words, knowledge of prefixes and suffixes)

- capitalization (e.g., in titles, sentence beginnings)

- punctuation (e.g., possessives, commas in a series, end of sentence punctuation)

- grammar (e.g., subject-verb agreement, verb tense, parts of speech)

Writing: This section of *TestSMART*™ includes descriptions of successful responses for several types of writing such as directions, compare/contrast, and persuasion. It also includes several writing prompts for student compositions.

Master Skills List/Correlation Chart: The language arts skills addressed in *TestSMART*™ are based on the language arts standards and/or test specifications from several different states. No two states have identical wordings for their skills lists, but there are strong similarities from one place to another. The Master Skills List for language arts (page 8) represents a synthesis of the language arts skills emphasized in various states. Teachers who use this book will recognize the skills that are stressed, even though the wording of a few objectives may vary slightly from that found in their own state's test specifications. The Master Skills Correlation Chart (page 9) offers a place to identify the skills common to both *TestSMART*™ and a specific state competency test.

Answer Keys: Complete answer keys for multiple-choice questions appear on pages 110-112.

Scoring Rubrics: The scoring rubrics on pages 120-122 provide important information for evaluating student-written compositions. (Note: If a state's assessment does not include a written composition, teachers may use the writing prompts in *TestSMART*™ as appropriate for their students.)

The sample rubrics allow teachers to rate the overall effectiveness and thoroughness of a student composition. For example, a four-point scoring rubric might allow a teacher to score papers on a scale from 1 (for the least effective essay) to 4 (for the most effective essay).

Note: States vary in their expectations for compositions. Some are required to be final rather than first drafts. Teachers should score their students' compositions according to their states' expectations or their own criteria.

Checklists for Student Writers: Students can use the checklists on pages 123-127 to self-check their own compositions. There are checklists for each type of writing included in *TestSMART™*, such as directions, compare/contrast, and persuasion.

How to Use this Book

Effective Test Preparation: What is the most effective way to prepare students for any English Language Arts competency test? Experienced educators know that the best test preparation includes three critical components—

- a strong curriculum that includes the content and skills to be tested

- effective and varied instructional methods that allow students to learn content and skills in many different ways

- targeted practice that familiarizes students with the specific content and format of the test they will take

Obviously, a strong curriculum and effective, varied instructional methods provide the foundation for all appropriate test preparation. Contrary to what some might believe, merely "teaching the test" performs a great disservice to students. Students must acquire knowledge, practice skills, and have specific educational experiences which can never be included on tests limited by time and in scope. For this reason, books like *TestSMART™* should never become the heart of the curriculum or a replacement for strong instructional methods.

Targeted Practice: *TestSMART™* does, however, address the final element of effective test preparation (targeted test practice) in the following ways—

- *TestSMART™* familiarizes students with the content usually included in competency tests.

- *TestSMART™* familiarizes students with the general format of such tests.

- When students become familiar with both the content and the format of a test, they know what to expect on the actual test. This, in turn, improves their chances for success.

Using *TestSMART™*: Used as part of the regular curriculum, *TestSMART™* allows teachers to—

- pretest skills needed for the actual test students will take

- determine students' areas of strength and/or weakness

- provide meaningful test-taking practice for students

- ease students' test anxiety

- communicate test expectations and content to parents

Master Skills List

I. Recognize correct and effective sentence structure in written text
   A. Recognize complete sentences as opposed to fragments and run-ons
   B. Recognize accurate combination of sentence parts to form complete structures

II. Recognize standard usage and appropriate word choice in written text
   A. Recognize correct spelling of words (e.g., contractions, frequently misspelled words)
   B. Recognize correct punctuation (e.g., sentence endings, abbreviations, quotations)
   C. Recognize appropriate capitalization (e.g., titles, sentence beginnings, proper nouns)
   D. Recognize standard grammar and usage (e.g., subject-verb agreement, parts of speech)

III. Produce an effective composition for a specific purpose
   A. Write for a variety of purposes and audiences
   B. Use voice and style appropriate to audience and purpose
   C. Use literary devices effectively (e.g., suspense, dialogue, figurative language)
   D. Organize ideas, use effective transitions, choose precise wording
   E. Demonstrate control of the English language (e.g., spelling, capitalization, usage)
   F. Use complete sentences (e.g., simple, complex, declarative, imperative)
   G. Employ editing strategies (e.g., elaboration, deletion, and rearrangement of words)
   H. Revise drafts for coherence, progression, and logical support of ideas

Master Skills Correlation Chart

Use this chart to identify the *TestSMART*™ skills included on a specific state competency test. Place a check mark next to those skills common to both.

I.	**Recognize correct and effective sentence structure in written text**	
	A. Recognize complete sentences as opposed to fragments and run-ons	
	B. Recognize accurate combination of sentence parts to form complete structures	
II.	**Recognize standard usage and appropriate word choice in written text**	
	A. Recognize correct spelling of words (e.g., contractions, frequently misspelled words)	
	B. Recognize correct punctuation (e.g., sentence endings, abbreviations, quotations)	
	C. Recognize appropriate capitalization (e.g., titles, sentence beginnings, proper nouns)	
	D. Recognize standard grammar and usage (e.g., subject-verb agreement, parts of speech)	
III.	**Produce an effective composition for a specific purpose**	
	A. Write for a variety of purposes and audiences	
	B. Use voice and style appropriate to audience and purpose	
	C. Use literary devices effectively (e.g., suspense, dialogue, figurative language)	
	D. Organize ideas, use effective transitions, choose precise wording	
	E. Demonstrate control of the English language (e.g., spelling, capitalization, usage)	
	F. Use complete sentences (e.g., simple, complex, declarative, imperative)	
	G. Employ editing strategies (e.g., elaboration, deletion, and rearrangement of words)	
	H. Revise drafts for coherence, progression, and logical support of ideas	

Notes

Sentence Structure

I. Recognize correct and effective sentence construction in written text

A. Recognize complete sentences as opposed to fragments and run-ons

B. Recognize accurate combination of sentence parts to form complete structures

Notes

Practice 1: Complete Sentences
Recognize complete sentences as opposed to fragments and run-ons (I.A)

Directions: Choose the sentence that is complete and written correctly.

1. A The pole vault is.
   B A field event requiring.
   C With the aid of a long pole.
   D She jumped over a high crossbar.

2. A The male quetzal bird has.
   B The quetzal bird has brilliant green and red colors.
   C And long flowing tail feathers.
   D A Central American bird?

3. A The Motorcycle Shop sells used.
   B 100 quality motorcycles.
   C We carry all makes and models.
   D Tires and batteries while you wait.

4. A Liking a hamburger and fries with catsup.
   B Hamburger, fries, served to us.
   C We ate hamburgers and fries.
   D With hamburgers we ate.

5. A The osprey, a fish-eating hawk.
   B And strong claws.
   C Having a short, hooked bill.
   D The osprey perched on a cactus.

6. A Black and white markings on the fur.
   B A cute, bearlike mammal.
   C I love its woolly fur!
   D From the mountains of China and Tibet.

7. A "Didn't you hear that loud crash of thunder?" asked Grace.
   B Grace asked, "Didn't you hear that loud?"
   C "Didn't you hear that loud crash of?"
   D Grace asked if we heard the loud crash of thunder did we?

8. A Without a hassle.
   B One easy number.
   C Call our free homework help line.
   D Staffed by actual teachers.

Practice 2: Complete Sentences

Recognize complete sentences as opposed to fragments and run-ons (I.A)

Directions: Choose the sentence that is complete and written correctly.

1. A Arthur Fiedler is one example of, isn't he?

   B A conductor leads musicians he or she makes sure that they play at the right speed.

   C Does a conductor direct musicians?

   D At the right speed and volume.

2. A It was a very, very old house it was built in 1789.

   B The novel *Something Upstairs*, a thriller.

   C The award-winning novelist Avi, this spooky book for ghost-story fans.

   D Would he be trapped in this haunted room forever?

3. A Skyscrapers in your city?

   B How tall the Empire State Building is!

   C I can name some skyscrapers two cities that have some are New York and Chicago.

   D The Sears Tower.

4. A Jim and I, we have.

   B Jim and I have never been to.

   C Neither Jim nor I.

   D Both Jim and I have seen that movie.

5. A "Mom, please don't hug me whenever my."

   B I don't like my mom to hug me in front of.

   C My mom always hugs me in front of my friends.

   D "It's embarrassing," I told my mom she still hugs me anyway.

6. A We bought bread, nail polish, and hair gel.

   B Including bread, nail polish, and hair gel.

   C These items: bread, nail polish, and hair gel?

   D Did you buy everything I hope so.

7. A No one knows how Stonehenge was constructed some people.

   B Who put the huge stones there?

   C Stonehenge, a circle of huge stones in England.

   D Standing upright from ancient times.

8. A An honor and a tradition.

   B Turning ten is the biggest event in a boy's.

   C Palmer isn't looking forward to his tenth birthday.

   D In the story *Wringer*, Palmer has to stop being afraid he stands up for what he believes in.

Practice 3: Complete Sentences

Recognize complete sentences as opposed to fragments and run-ons (I.A)

Directions: Choose the sentence that is complete and written correctly.

1. **A** How his dog's coat shines!

   B My friend Brandon has an Irish setter it has a very shiny coat.

   C A silky reddish-brown coat.

   D Named Red, because it has a silky red coat.

2. **A** A haircut, now it's short.

   B By December my hair will be long again I'm going to let it grow long again.

   C How do you like my short haircut?

   D Does that mean that you don't like it my short haircut?

3. **A** A new tire for my bike.

   B Should I buy a new tire?

   C Or just replace the tire tube?

   D I have a flat I can't ride my bike to school until I get a new tire.

4. **A** Henry is building a model it is of the Great Wall of China.

   B One of the Seven Wonders of the World.

   C Henry carved wood and painted it to look like the Great Wall.

   D Probably the best project in the class.

5. **A** Andrew cried at his desk I heard him.

   B Upset about losing his retainer.

   C Found it in the cafeteria, left on his lunch tray.

   D Our English teacher asked him what was wrong.

6. **A** Reading the rules in every class.

   B About not being tardy, or forgetting your supplies.

   C Teachers all saying the same thing.

   D On the first day of school, we learned about the rules.

7. **A** Small pony with a long thick mane.

   B I've always wanted a Shetland pony my mom said no.

   C These are small ponies with thick manes and tails.

   D Coming from the Shetland Islands.

8. **A** I laughed; he didn't.

   B Ethan sitting in the wrong class; for about 10 minutes.

   C The teacher said; Ethan you don't have this class until tomorrow.

   D Turning red, getting up quickly; he didn't laugh but I did.

Practice 4: Identify Fragments
Recognize complete sentences as opposed to fragments and run-ons (I.A)

Directions: Read each passage. Use each passage to answer the question below it.

> (1)What are the fashion fads this year? (2)Fads are the clothes or shoes that everyone wants to have. (3)Blue jeans and tennis shoes. (4)The newest styles of these items are always popular.

1. Which of these choices is NOT a complete sentence?

    A 1
    B 2
    C 3
    D 4

> (1)What does the expression "hang out" mean? (2)To "hang out" with friends means that you spend time together. (3)Can you think of something that you enjoy doing with? (4)Do you ever hang out with your friends after school?

2. Which of these choices is NOT a complete sentence?

    A 1
    B 2
    C 3
    D 4

> (1)To make a grilled cheese sandwich. (2)You need a slice of American cheese and two pieces of buttered bread. (3)You put the cheese between the bread slices. (4)Place the bread slices so the buttered sides face out. (5)Grill both sides of the sandwich in a pan.

3. Which of these choices is NOT a complete sentence?

    A 1
    B 2
    C 4
    D 5

Practice 5: Identify Fragments
Recognize complete sentences as opposed to fragments and run-ons (I.A)

Directions: Read each passage. Use each passage to answer the question below it.

> (1)Never leave food out of the refrigerator for more than two hours. (2)Food can spoil. (3)From bacteria. (4)Bacteria multiply quickly. (5)To prevent your picnic food from spoiling, pack it in ice.

1. Which of these choices is NOT a complete sentence?

   A 2
   B 3
   C 4
   D 5

> (1)Once more the priest, called the Dagda, touched his harp. (2)But very, very softly. (3)Music stole forth as soft as dreams and as sweet as joy. (4)It was the magic music of sleep. (5)The young warriors drooped in their seats and closed their eyes. (6)The Dagda and his golden-haired warriors crept away, and came in safety to their own homes again.
>
> *Adapted from the Irish legend, "The Dagda's Harp"*

2. Which of these choices is NOT a complete sentence?

   A 2
   B 3
   C 4
   D 6

> (1)What is a balanced diet? (2)It contains a variety of foods that a person needs. (3)To stay healthy. (4)A balanced diet includes protein, vitamins, carbohydrates, fats, and minerals. (5)A balanced diet provides energy and helps with body functions.

3. Which of these choices is NOT a complete sentence?

   A 1
   B 2
   C 3
   D 5

Practice 6: Identify Fragments

Recognize complete sentences as opposed to fragments and run-ons (I.A)

Directions: Read each passage. Use each passage to answer the question below it.

> Dear Mrs. Hill,
>
> (1)My mom said that she can participate in the Career Day program. (2)On Monday, February 15. (3)She will be speaking about her job as a graphic designer. (4)How long of a presentation should she plan?
>
> Sincerely,
Gabriel Hernandez

1. Which of these choices is NOT a complete sentence?

    A 1
    B 2
    C 3
    D 4

> (1)*The Watsons Go to Birmingham* is a fictional novel, but it includes some factual events. (2)It was written by Christopher Paul Curtis and is his first novel. (3)The main character, Kenny, is ten years old. (4)It's a hilarious book. (5)Do you enjoy humor? (6)Funny, while it is about a dark moment in American history.

2. Which of these choices is NOT a complete sentence?

    A 2
    B 3
    C 5
    D 6

> (1)My school has an after-school tutoring program. (2)Teachers will work with you on math, reading, and. (3)You can get all of your homework done during tutoring. (4)My grades have improved as a result of tutoring.

3. Which of these choices is NOT a complete sentence?

    A 1
    B 2
    C 3
    D 4

Practice 7: Combining Sentences

Recognize accurate combination of sentence parts to form complete structures (I.B)

Directions: Read the paragraph. Some parts are underlined. The questions ask about the underlined parts.

> Do earthworms really improve soil? They sure do. No other organism can break down as much dead plant and animal material. These wriggly animals burrow through the ground.
> (1)
> Eating decayed materials such as dead leaves and plant roots. The long, narrow tunnels
> (2)
> earthworms make can be as deep as 6 feet, and they create air pockets that provide oxygen to a growing plant's roots and also improve drainage. On top of all that, earthworms leave behind
> (3)
> an organic waste. Rich with nutrients that plants need to grow.
> (4)
>
> *Adapted from The Ohio State University; College of Food, Agricultural and Environmental Sciences, 1999*

1. Which of these is the best way to write parts 1 and 2 in one sentence?

   A These wriggly animals burrow through the ground eating decayed materials, such as dead leaves, and plant roots.

   B These wriggly animals burrow through the ground eating decayed materials such as dead leaves and plant roots.

   C These wriggly animals: burrow through the ground eating decayed materials such as dead leaves and plant roots.

   D No mistake

2. Which of these is the best way to write parts 3 and 4 in one sentence?

   A On top of all that; earthworms leave behind an organic waste rich with nutrients that plants need to grow.

   B On top of all that earthworms leave behind, an organic waste rich with nutrients that plants need to grow.

   C On top of all that, earthworms leave behind an organic waste rich with nutrients that plants need to grow.

   D No mistake

Practice 8: Combining Sentences

Recognize accurate combination of sentence parts to form complete structures (I.B)

Directions: Read the paragraph. Some parts are underlined. The questions ask about the underlined parts.

Why do some birds fly in a "V"? Canada geese and other water birds. Such as ducks,
(1)   (2)
pelicans, and cranes use the distinct "V" formation to get a little lift. These birds move
through the air with their wings as they fly and leave a whirl of wind behind them. Each
goose, flying a little to the side and rear of the goose ahead of it, rides the draft of air created
by the goose in front of it. That way, every bird in the flock except the "lead" goose saves
about one-third of its energy by flying in a V-shape. Being the leader is the toughest. Job so
(3)   (4)
the geese take turns. Sometimes they trade off so often that they fly in long, wavy lines
instead of V's.

Adapted from The Ohio State University; College of Food, Agricultural and Environmental Sciences, 1999

---

1. Which of these is the best way to write parts 1 and 2 in one sentence?

   A Canada geese and other water birds: such as ducks, pelicans, and cranes use the distinct "V" formation to get a little lift.

   B Canada geese and other water birds such as ducks, pelicans, and cranes use the distinct "V" formation to get a little lift.

   C Canada geese and other water birds such as ducks, pelicans, and cranes; use the distinct "V" formation to get a little lift.

   D No mistake

2. Which of these is the best way to write parts 3 and 4 in one sentence?

   A Being the leader is the toughest job, so the geese take turns.

   B Being the leader, is the toughest job, so the geese take turns.

   C Being the leader; is the toughest job so the geese take turns.

   D No mistake

Practice 9: Combining Sentences

Recognize accurate combination of sentence parts to form complete structures (I.B)

Directions: Read the letter. Some parts are underlined. The questions ask about the underlined parts.

Dear Mr. Dean,

Did you know that there are quite a few good Web sites. Providing information about the
    (1)   (2)
Olympics? Some sites have sounds and images. You can research facts on the past, present,

and future of the Olympics. I would be glad to show the class some of the sites I have found

helpful. The Internet is an excellent resource. For our upcoming integrated unit about the
             (3)   (4)
Olympics.

Yours truly,

Zoe Peterson

---

1. Which of these is the best way to write parts 1 and 2 in one sentence?

   A Did you know that there are quite a few good Web sites; providing information about the Olympics.

   B Did you know that there are quite a few good Web sites providing information about the Olympics?

   C There are quite a few good Web sites providing information about the Olympics did you know that?

   D No mistake

2. Which of these is the best way to write parts 3 and 4 in one sentence?

   A About the Olympics the Internet is an excellent resource for our upcoming integrated unit.

   B The Internet is an excellent resource, for our upcoming integrated unit, about the Olympics?

   C The Internet is an excellent resource for our upcoming integrated unit about the Olympics.

   D No mistake

Practice 10: Sentence Editing

Recognize accurate combination of sentence parts to form complete structures (I.B)

Directions: Read the passage. Decide which is the best way to write each underlined part. Mark the letter for your answer. If the underlined part is correctly written, mark "No mistake."

> There was once an old king so wise and kind that a good fairy visited him. She asked him to name the dearest wish of his heart. His wish was for his son, Prince Cherry.
>
> <u>Choose what I shall give him. I can make him the most powerful prince in the world, said the fairy.</u> (1)
>
> "I want only that he shall be good. <u>Of what use will it be to him to be handsome, rich, or powerful? If he grows into a bad man?</u> Make him the best prince in the world!" commanded the king. (2)
>
> "I cannot make him good," said the fairy. "He must do that for himself. I can give him good advice and be his best friend, but I cannot make him good unless he wills it."
>
> *Adapted from the tale, "Prince Cherry"*

1. **A** "Choose what I shall give him. I can make him the most powerful prince in the world," said the fairy.

   B "I can make him the most powerful prince in the world," said the fairy. Choose what I shall give him.

   C "Choose what I shall give him." I can make him the most powerful prince in the world, said the fairy.

   D No mistake

2. **A** Of what use will it be to him to be handsome, rich, or powerful. If he grows into a bad man?

   B If he grows into a bad man. Of what use will it be to him to be handsome, rich, or powerful?

   C Of what use will it be to him to be handsome, rich, or powerful if he grows into a bad man?

   D No mistake

Practice 11: Sentence Editing

Recognize accurate combination of sentence parts to form complete structures (I.B)

Directions: Read the passage. Decide which is the best way to write each underlined part. Mark the letter for your answer. If the underlined part is correctly written, mark "No mistake."

Connor spent more time on homework than he wanted to. He would rather be outside playing basketball with his buddies. He moaned to his older sister, Alexis, about his problem.

"You need to get organized," Alexis told him. "Make sure you bring home all the books
_____(1)_____
and papers. That you need to do your homework. Write down your assignments carefully."

That advice made sense to Connor. He often wasted time remembering his exact assignments.

His sister suggested that he talk over his assignments with a friend. And even that he work
_____(2)_____
with a friend when appropriate. "As long as your friend doesn't become a distraction to you," Alexis added.

Finally, Alexis encouraged Connor to get as much work done at school as possible. With these new options, Connor felt better about doing homework.

---

1. **A** All the books and papers that you need to do your homework. Make sure you bring home

   B Make sure you bring home all the books and papers that you need. To do your homework.

   C Make sure you bring home all the books and papers that you need to do your homework.

   D No mistake

2. **A** With a friend when appropriate; his sister suggested that he talk over his assignments.

   B His sister suggested that he talk over his assignments with a friend, and even that he work with a friend when appropriate.

   C His sister suggested, "That he talk over his assignments with a friend and even that he work with a friend when appropriate."

   D No mistake

23

Practice 12: Sentence Editing

Recognize accurate combination of sentence parts to form complete structures (I.B)

Directions: Read the passage. Decide which is the best way to write each underlined part. Mark the letter for your answer. If the underlined part is correctly written, mark "No mistake."

Dear Mrs. Zwart,

   This letter is to thank you and your company for donating; paper products for our sixth-
      (1)
grade class picnic. The picnic was a huge success. Some students and teachers received

awards, and a good time was had by all. This event would not have been possible. Without the
                                          (2)
generosity of companies such as yours. On behalf of the sixth-grade class at Rhine Middle

School, I extend our appreciation.

                     Sincerely,

                     Jeremy Brockington

---

1. **A** This letter is to thank you and your company for donating: paper products for our sixth-grade class picnic.

   B For donating paper products for our sixth-grade class picnic, this letter is. To thank you and your company.

   C This letter is to thank you and your company for donating paper products for our sixth-grade class picnic.

   D No mistake

2. **A** Without the generosity of companies such as yours; this event would not have been possible.

   B This event would not have been possible without the generosity of companies such as yours.

   C This event would not have been possible without the generosity. Of companies such as yours.

   D No mistake

Practice 13: Combining Ideas

Recognize accurate combination of sentence parts to form complete structures (I.B)

Directions: Read the sentences. Decide which answer *best* combines the ideas into one sentence.

Pam brought snacks.

She brought these snacks.

She brought pretzels, popcorn, potato chips, and crackers.

1. **A** These snacks: pretzels, popcorn, potato chips, and crackers.

 B Pretzels, popcorn, potato chips, and crackers are what Pam brought these snacks.

 C Pam, she brought snacks and the snacks were these: pretzels, popcorn, potato chips, and crackers.

 D Pam brought these snacks: pretzels, popcorn, potato chips, and crackers.

Noah was a football player.

Noah was great at playing football.

But he was even better at public speaking than at playing football.

2. **A** Noah was a football player and he was a great football player but he was better at public speaking than at playing football.

 B Noah, a better public speaker, was great at playing football.

 C Noah was a great football player; he was an even better public speaker.

 D Noah played great football, but he was even better at public speaking?

Send your application to Mrs. Jones at 827 Crestview.

Send it to Dallas, Texas.

The application deadline is March 2001.

3. **A** Send your application, the deadline is March 2001, to Mrs. Jones at 827 Crestview, send it to Dallas, Texas.

 B Send your application before March 2001, to Mrs. Jones, 827 Crestview, Dallas, Texas.

 C To Dallas Texas send: your application, to Mrs. Jones, 827 Crestview, send it by March 2001.

 D By March 2001, send your application to: Mrs. Jones 827 Crestview Dallas Texas.

He asked this question.

He asked, "Did we win?"

It was Joey who asked.

4. **A** He asked this question Joey asked, "Did we win?"

 B It was Joey he asked this question: "Did we win?"

 C "Did we win?" this is the question that Joey asked.

 D Joey asked, "Did we win?"

Practice 14: Combining Ideas

Recognize accurate combination of sentence parts to form complete structures (I.B)

Directions: Read the sentences. Decide which answer *best* combines the ideas into one sentence.

Isabella likes two things.
She likes talking on the telephone.
She likes shopping.

1. **A** Isabella likes: talking on the telephone and shopping.
   B Isabella likes two things: talking on the telephone and shopping.
   C Isabella likes: two things, talking on the telephone and shopping.
   D Isabella likes two things she likes talking on the telephone and shopping.

I told you, Steven.
It wouldn't rain.
I was talking about today.

2. **A** Steven, today I told you, it wouldn't rain.
   B I told you, Steven, it wouldn't rain I was talking about today.
   C I told you, Steven, that it wouldn't rain today.
   D I told Steven that it wouldn't rain I was talking about today.

Victoria is my sister.
She is my youngest sister.
She has always been artistic.

3. **A** Victoria is my sister she is my youngest sister and has always been artistic.
   B My youngest sister is Victoria she has always been artistic.
   C My youngest sister, Victoria; she has always been artistic.
   D Victoria, my youngest sister, has always been artistic.

Island of the Blue Dolphins is an adventure story.
It won the Newbery Award.
The award is for literature.

4. **A** *Island of the Blue Dolphins*, an adventure story, won the Newbery Award for literature.
   B *Island of the Blue Dolphins* is an adventure story it won the Newbery Award for literature.
   C It won the Newbery Award, *Island of the Blue Dolphins*, for literature.
   D An adventure story, *Island of the Blue Dolphins*, it won the Newbery Award for literature.

Practice 15: Combining Ideas
Recognize accurate combination of sentence parts to form complete structures (I.B)

Directions: Read the sentences. Decide which answer *best* combines the ideas into one sentence.

The magazine article was about my two favorite subjects.

I like music.

I like fashion.

1. **A** The magazine article was about my two favorite subjects: music and fashion.

    B The magazine article was about my two favorite subjects; I like music; I like fashion.

    C The magazine article, about my two favorite subjects, was about music and fashion.

    D I like music and fashion, however, the magazine article was about my two favorite subjects.

The ibis is a storklike bird.

It is a wading bird.

The ibis lives in tropical regions.

2. **A** The ibis is a storklike bird and a wading bird the ibis lives in tropical regions.

    B In tropical regions, the ibis is a storklike bird it is a wading bird.

    C Being wading and storklike, the ibis lives in tropical regions.

    D The ibis, a storklike wading bird, lives in tropical regions.

Candy yelled.

She yelled to Ron.

"Watch out for that hole in the ground!"

3. **A** Candy she yelled to Ron, "Watch out for that hole in the ground!"

    B Ron yelled at Candy. "Watch out for that hole in the ground!"

    C Candy yelled: Ron, watch out for that hole in the ground!

    D Candy yelled, "Ron, watch out for that hole in the ground!"

The Tiber is a river.

The Tiber River is in Italy.

It flows through Rome.

4. **A** The Tiber, a river, is in Italy it flows through Rome.

    B The Tiber River flows through Rome, Italy.

    C Flowing through Rome, Italy, the Tiber River is in Italy.

    D The Tiber is a river in Italy it flows through Rome.

Practice 16: Revising Paragraphs
Recognize correct and effective sentence structure in written text (I)

Directions: Read the passage. Use the passage to answer the questions below it.

> (1)How much should your school backpack weigh? (2)Doctors say you should carry no more than 10 percent of your body weight in your backpack. (3)So, if you weigh 80 pounds, your backpack should weigh no more than 8 pounds. (4)You should support this weight with your back and abdominal muscles to prevent shoulder or neck injuries. (5)How can you reduce and lessen the load? (6)Put the heaviest books closer to your body. (7)Do this when you pack. (8)Carry only the books that you need. (9)Leave video games, CDs, and extra items at home. (10)Work on homework every night. (11)To avoid lugging a backpack full of books home at one time.

1. Which sentence says the same thing twice?

    A 1
    B 3
    C 5
    D 7

2. Which of these is NOT a complete sentence?

    A 2
    B 6
    C 8
    D 11

3. What is the best way to combine 6 and 7 into one sentence?

    A You should put the heaviest books closer to your body when you pack?
    B Put the heaviest books closer to your body; when you pack.
    C Put the heaviest books closest to your body when you pack.
    D Do you put the heaviest books closer to your body when you pack.

Practice 17: Revising Paragraphs
Recognize correct and effective sentence structure in written text (I)

Directions: Read the passage. Use the passage to answer the questions below it.

> (1)Soccer may be dangerous to and could hurt your brain. (2)Heading the ball in soccer may cause injury to your brain, according to researchers. (3)Children under the age of 14 are especially at risk. (4)As they do not have the muscular or skeletal maturity to head the ball. (5)Some symptoms of injury include concussions and headaches. (6)Are protective measures recommended? (7)Measures such as the use of helmets and lightweight balls?

1. Which sentence says the same thing twice?

   A 1

   B 3

   C 5

   D 6

2. Which of these is NOT a complete sentence?

   A 2

   B 3

   C 4

   D 5

3. What is the best way to combine parts 6 and 7 into one sentence?

   A Are they recommended, protective measures such as helmets and lightweight balls?

   B Protective measures: such as the use of helmets and lightweight balls are recommended.

   C Are protective measures such as the use of helmets and lightweight balls, they recommend that?

   D Are protective measures such as the use of helmets and lightweight balls recommended?

Practice 18: Revising Paragraphs

Recognize correct and effective sentence structure in written text (I)

Directions: Read the passage. Use the passage to answer the questions below it.

> (1)Do you communicate with your parents? (2)Do you communicate daily? (3)As a busy teen, you may need to make time to talk. (4)Here are some ideas and here are some tips for sharing opinions, thoughts, and information with your family. (5)Share something about your activities. (6)With your parents each day. (7)Answer their questions with more than "yes" or "no" answers. (8)Take advantage of "wait" time, such as the time you spend in the car, to talk with your parents. (9)Participate with your parents in activities that encourage conversation, such as playing board games and sports, or attending school events.

1. Which sentence says the same thing twice?

    A 1

    B 4

    C 5

    D 8

2. Which of these is NOT a complete sentence?

    A 2

    B 3

    C 4

    D 6

3. What is the best way to combine parts 1 and 2 into one sentence?

    A Do you communicate with your parents daily?

    B With your parents, do you communicate, and each day?

    C Communicate with your parents, do you each day?

    D Do you communicate with your parents daily each day?

Standard Usage

II. Recognize standard usage and appropriate word choice in written text

A. Recognize correct spelling of words (e.g., contractions, frequently misspelled words)

B. Recognize correct punctuation (e.g., sentence endings, abbreviations, quotations)

C. Recognize appropriate capitalization (e.g., titles, sentence beginnings, proper nouns)

D. Recognize standard grammar and usage (e.g., subject-verb agreement, parts of speech)

Practice 1: Frequently Misspelled Words

Recognize correct spelling of words (II.A)

Directions: Read the sentence. Look for the correct spelling of the word that belongs in the sentence.

1. My mom does not like my brother and me to _____.

   A argew

   B argu

   C argue

   D argeu

2. Amanda's floral dress is _____.

   A beautaful

   B beautifull

   C beutiful

   D beautiful

3. Daniel asked, "What day of the week is my birthday, according to your _____?"

   A calindar

   B calendar

   C calender

   D calander

4. I wish Anna would _____ her temper.

   A controle

   B control

   C controll

   D cuntrol

5. Sammy's dog developed a skin _____.

   A dizease

   B disese

   C disaese

   D disease

6. Cheryl ate an _____ slice of hot pie.

   A excellent

   B excelent

   C excellant

   D exsellent

Practice 2: Frequently Misspelled Words

Recognize correct spelling of words (II.A)

Directions: Read the sentence. Look for the correct spelling of the word that belongs in the sentence.

1. Is Sophia your _____?

   A neece
   B neise
   C niece
   D neice

2. Tyler calmly shared his _____ with his father.

   A opinoin
   B opinyun
   C opinion
   D openion

3. The color blue is my _____ choice for decorating.

   A persinal
   B personal
   C personel
   D pursonal

4. Were you ever a victim of _____?

   A prejudice
   B prejeduce
   C prejadice
   D prejudace

5. I _____ should have studied for this test.

   A probablly
   B probly
   C prolly
   D probably

6. A study area should be _____ so the student can concentrate.

   A quiet
   B quite
   C quiat
   D queit

Practice 3: Frequently Misspelled Words
Recognize correct spelling of words (II.A)

Directions: Read the sentence. Look for the correct spelling of the word that belongs in the sentence.

1. Taking out the garbage is my new
   _____.

   A   responsibillity
   B   responsability
   C   responsibility
   D   responsibilty

2. Brianna is a very _____ and hard-working student.

   A   serius
   B   serious
   C   seriuos
   D   seerious

3. He was _____ sorry about arriving so late.

   A   sinserely
   B   sinceerly
   C   sincerly
   D   sincerely

4. This heart locket is very _____ because my grandma gave it to me.

   A   speshal
   B   special
   C   specail
   D   speshel

5. Most athletes practice often to _____ at their chosen sport.

   A   suceed
   B   suckseed
   C   succeed
   D   succede

6. At what _____ does water boil?

   A   temperture
   B   tempurature
   C   tempature
   D   temperature

Practice 4: Editing for Spelling
Recognize correct spelling of words (II.A)

Directions: Read the sentences. Some words are underlined. Find the underlined word in each sentence that is spelled wrong. Mark the letter for your answer.

1. I <u>truley</u> liked that <u>strawberry</u> shake with <u>whipped</u> <u>cream</u>.
   Ⓐ   Ⓑ   Ⓒ   Ⓓ

2. Where did Logan find such a <u>colorful</u> and <u>unuseual</u> <u>pair</u> of <u>sneakers</u>?
                               Ⓐ   Ⓑ Ⓒ   Ⓓ

3. The only <u>vegtables</u> that Haley will eat are <u>potatoes</u>, <u>broccoli</u>, and <u>corn</u>.
          Ⓐ   Ⓑ   Ⓒ   Ⓓ

4. That green <u>alien</u> <u>costume</u> that Sydney wore <u>sure</u> looked <u>weerd</u>.
         Ⓐ   Ⓑ   Ⓒ   Ⓓ

5. You should always <u>yeild</u> to <u>oncoming</u> <u>traffic</u> at that <u>intersection</u>.
              Ⓐ   Ⓑ   Ⓒ   Ⓓ

6. I should have taken my <u>cousin's</u> <u>advise</u> and <u>purchased</u> a larger <u>backpack</u>.
             Ⓐ   Ⓑ   Ⓒ   Ⓓ

Practice 5: Editing for Spelling

Recognize correct spelling of words (II.A)

Directions: Read the sentences. Some words are underlined. Find the underlined word in each sentence that is spelled wrong. Mark the letter for your answer.

1. William <u>hoped</u> that his <u>mathematics</u> <u>homework</u> was <u>acurate</u>.
       Ⓐ   Ⓑ   Ⓒ   Ⓓ

2. We are <u>studying</u> about the <u>anchent</u> Mayan <u>civilization</u> in <u>history</u> class.
       Ⓐ   Ⓑ   Ⓒ   Ⓓ

3. How <u>relieved</u> John was to <u>avoid</u> a <u>bitter</u> <u>arguement</u>!
       Ⓐ   Ⓑ Ⓒ   Ⓓ

4. Many <u>couragous</u> men and women have <u>unselfishly</u> <u>served</u> our <u>country</u>.
       Ⓐ   Ⓑ   Ⓒ   Ⓓ

5. Sean said, "I <u>definitly</u> will not <u>attend</u> band <u>practice</u> on <u>Saturday</u> morning."
       Ⓐ   Ⓑ   Ⓒ   Ⓓ

6. I will <u>certainly</u> try out for the <u>track</u> and <u>basketball</u> teams when I am in <u>eigth</u> grade.
       Ⓐ   Ⓑ   Ⓒ   Ⓓ

Practice 6: Editing for Spelling
Recognize correct spelling of words (II.A)

Directions: Read the sentences. Some words are underlined. Find the underlined word in each sentence that is spelled wrong. Mark the letter for your answer.

1. Christi said, "I don't mean to <u>embarass</u> you, but you have some <u>gum</u> <u>stuck</u> to the bottom of your <u>shoe</u>."
   Ⓐ   Ⓑ Ⓒ   Ⓓ

2. Mrs. Mencio never <u>fully</u> <u>ansered</u> my question <u>regarding</u> the cost of our <u>field</u> trip.
   Ⓐ   Ⓑ   Ⓒ   Ⓓ

3. Amber could not <u>beleive</u> that her <u>soccer</u> <u>uniform</u> had <u>gotten</u> so dirty.
   Ⓐ   Ⓑ Ⓒ   Ⓓ

4. What <u>type</u> of <u>bisness</u> does Evan's <u>grandfather</u> <u>own</u>?
   Ⓐ   Ⓑ   Ⓒ   Ⓓ

5. My English and <u>science</u> teachers have very <u>diffrent</u> <u>ideas</u> about <u>assigning</u> homework.
   Ⓐ   Ⓑ Ⓒ   Ⓓ

6. Savannah <u>thought</u> the <u>author's</u> book, although <u>fasinating</u>, was <u>extremely</u> long.
   Ⓐ   Ⓑ   Ⓒ   Ⓓ

Practice 7: Correct Punctuation
Recognize correct punctuation (II.B)

Directions: Read the sentence. Decide which punctuation mark the sentence needs. Mark the letter for your answer.

1. Dylan how long did band practice last?

   (A) ;   (B) .   (C) ?   (D) ,

2. Katherine said "I felt lonely; Mrs. Simms comforted me."

   (A) ,   (B) ;   (C) "   (D) .

3. How wonderful the air-conditioned house feels when it's hot outside

   (A) .   (B) ,   (C) ?   (D) !

4. Sierra yelled, "Christian, don't forget that you owe me two dollars

   (A) ."   (B) ,"   (C) ?"   (D) !"

5. Is that Mr. Nortons microscope?

   (A) '   (B) ;   (C) ?   (D) !

6. Sen Booker spoke about the state's energy crisis.

   (A) ?   (B) ,   (C) .   (D) !

Practice 8: Correct Punctuation

Recognize correct punctuation (II.B)

Directions: Read the sentence. Decide which punctuation mark the sentence needs. Mark the letter for your answer.

1. Antonio did you enjoy your trip to New Hampshire?

   (A) .   (B) ,   (C) ?   (D) !

2. Here's what I need to make a cake eggs, milk, flour, and oil.

   (A) .   (B) ,   (C) ?   (D) :

3. How I crave a big, spicy slice of pizza

   (A) .   (B) ,   (C) ?   (D) !

4. As for me I'd rather play basketball than watch TV.

   (A) .   (B) ,   (C) ?   (D) !

5. Mariah's volunteer work at the animal shelter began October 14 2001.

   (A) .   (B) ?   (C) ,   (D) !

6. I had to sweep stack boxes, and organize the shelves in our garage.

   (A) .   (B) !   (C) ?   (D) ,

Practice 9: Correct Punctuation

Recognize correct punctuation (II.B)

Directions: Read the sentence. Decide which punctuation mark the sentence needs. Mark the letter for your answer.

1. Erin moaned, Can't we watch a comedy instead of a drama?"
   Ⓐ .   Ⓑ ,   Ⓒ ?   Ⓓ "

2. The magnetic needle of a compass points north
   Ⓐ .   Ⓑ ,   Ⓒ ?   Ⓓ !

3. Codys thoughtful gesture made me smile.
   Ⓐ .   Ⓑ ,   Ⓒ '   Ⓓ ?

4. My father will travel to Utah Florida, Colorado, and California this month.
   Ⓐ ,   Ⓑ .   Ⓒ ?   Ⓓ !

5. It was Martin Luther King, Jr. who said these words "The time is always right to do what is right."
   Ⓐ .   Ⓑ :   Ⓒ ?   Ⓓ !

6. Well I didn't mean to break that lamp.
   Ⓐ .   Ⓑ ,   Ⓒ ?   Ⓓ !

40

Practice 10: End of Sentence Punctuation

Recognize correct punctuation (II.B)

Directions: Choose the word and punctuation mark that belong at the end of each sentence. Mark your answer.

1. This music book is _____

   A Jenna's.
   B Jenna's!
   C Jenna's
   D Jennas?

2. How horrible my dream _____

   A was
   B was!
   C was?
   D was,

3. Jeremy asked, "What time does math class _____

   A begin."
   B begin"
   C begin!"
   D begin?"

4. Where did you buy that silver purse _____

   A Amanda
   B Amanda.
   C , Amanda?
   D , Amanda!

5. Software refers to programs that computers can _____

   A run
   B run,
   C run.
   D run?

6. Can't we go to the movies with _____

   A Ryan!
   B Ryan?
   C Ryan
   D Ryan.

7. Is that black wallet Mr. _____

   A Wright's,
   B Wright's.
   C Wrights.
   D Wright's?

8. Jada exclaimed, "How friendly all my teammates _____

   A are.
   B are!"
   C are?"
   D are."

Practice 11: End of Sentence Punctuation

Recognize correct punctuation (II.B)

Directions: Choose the word and punctuation mark that belong at the end of each sentence. Mark your answer.

1. How do you define _____

   A freedom,
   B freedom.
   C freedom?
   D freedom

2. Julian stated, "Football practice will be held at the high school _____

   A field?"
   B field!"
   C field."
   D field"

3. How annoying Leslie can _____

   A be
   B be?
   C be!
   D be,

4. Life science isn't my best subject, but it is _____

   A Victor's.
   B Victors'.
   C Victor.
   D Victors.

5. Wasn't Buddha an ancient holy man in _____

   A India?
   B India.
   C India
   D India,

6. Please help me move this _____

   A couch?
   B couch.
   C couch
   D couch,

7. Charles yelled, "That river is _____

   A freezing!
   B freezing.
   C freezing."
   D freezing!"

8. Wouldn't it be cool to have a black _____

   A light.
   B light!
   C light
   D light?

Practice 12: End of Sentence Punctuation

Recognize correct punctuation (II.B)

Directions: Choose the word and punctuation mark that belong at the end of each sentence. Mark your answer.

1. What did the doctor say about your _____

   A rash?
   B rash.
   C rash!
   D rash

2. Never shy, Claire enjoys singing in front of _____

   A others
   B others,
   C others?
   D others.

3. My grandfather asked, "Do you have a _____

   A hammer,"
   B hammer?"
   C hammer"
   D hammer!"

4. Patrick Henry exclaimed, "Give me liberty, or give me _____

   A death"
   B death,"
   C death?"
   D death!"

5. That mess isn't mine, it's my _____

   A brotherses.
   B brothers.
   C brother's.
   D brothers!

6. How elegant their home _____

   A was.
   B was?
   C was!
   D was

7. In *Frankenstein*, a scientist creates a gigantic _____

   A monster?
   B monster.
   C monster,
   D monster

8. My nephew thought those golf clubs were _____

   A mine's.
   B mine?
   C mine.
   D mines!

Practice 13: Edit for Capitalization
Recognize appropriate capitalization (II.C)

Directions: Read the sentences. Decide which sentence has a word that needs a capital letter.

1. A Please tell John daniel Simmons that his book order has arrived.
   B He can pick it up at the Book Nook.
   C We are located at the corner of Canal Street and 7th Avenue.
   D The bookstore is closed on Sundays.

2. A My Grandmother Lucia was an outstanding baker; her specialty was pie.
   B "Andy is going to eat dessert with us," said Katie.
   C She made a cherry pie using her grandmother's recipe.
   D "Will you stay for lunch, Bill?" asked mother.

3. A I'd like to order a Coke.
   B He is a sixth grader at Deston middle School.
   C His school is located exactly two miles from Burger Time.
   D Burger Time is the largest fast food chain in the U.S. and Canada.

4. A We purchase a newspaper every Sunday.
   B The article was titled, "Five Ways to Organize Your Stuff."
   C My father's business was highlighted in the *Chicago tribune*.
   D Andrew, do you ever read the newspaper?

5. A She has taken lessons at Cummings Art School.
   B Erin is interested in painting, especially with acrylic.
   C Her favorite painting is called "Starry Night."
   D It was created by a dutch artist.

6. A We had horrible flooding in South Texas.
   B Mr. Dabon exclaimed, "look at that lightning!"
   C The Perdenales River was well above its banks.
   D Trudy and Xavier Gaston lost electrical power due to the storm.

7. A James attended the annual thanksgiving parade.
   B He was quite impressed by the Tucson High School marching band.
   C Police blocked off Central Avenue, part of the parade route.
   D James saw Mr. and Mrs. Hernandez and their daughter Estella.

8. A A soprano is a singer with a high voice.
   B Shall I try out for the Trinity church Choir?
   C Our practices are held every Thursday evening in the church's activity room.
   D Mr. and Mrs. Brenner are our choir sponsors.

44

Practice 14: Edit for Capitalization

Recognize appropriate capitalization (II.C)

Directions: Read the sentences. Decide which sentence has a word that needs a capital letter.

1. **A** Betsy's college has a computer lab.
   B My niece Amy and my nephew Tyler are from Atlanta, Georgia.
   C The last time I saw her was June.
   D My sister Betsy goes to boulder Junior College.

2. **A** Uncle Donald is a carpenter.
   B My uncle built cabinets for aunt Trudy.
   C My uncle asked, "What color shall I paint these cabinets?"
   D My aunt wants white cabinets.

3. **A** Why do kids like extreme sports?
   B Some kids are happier riding their skateboards than dealing with traditional team sports.
   C Snowboarding became an official Olympic event at the 1998 nagano Games.
   D Kids suffer the most injuries in the following six sports: basketball, football, baseball, softball, soccer, and gymnastics.

4. **A** The first Europeans to cross the Gobi Desert were Venetian explorer Marco Polo, his father, and his uncle.
   B Were fossilized dinosaur eggs found in the desert?
   C The gobi Desert is in Mongolia.
   D Finds include artifacts from the Bronze Age.

5. **A** Why are Ancient egyptians the best known mummy-makers?
   B Climate more than skill first preserved the Egyptians' dead.
   C Desert winds and hot sand dried corpses out.
   D A mummy is an old, dead body.

6. **A** Ajax was the son of Telamon, a king.
   B After Achilles, Ajax was the most powerful of the Greek heroes.
   C He was a huge man; he is often called the "wall" of the Greeks.
   D Ajax was a hero of the Trojan war.

7. **A** Before you can learn to draw comic books, you have to learn how to be an artist.
   B "Pick up your pencil and draw everything around you," advises Gerry Alanguilan.
   C Buy an anatomy book such as *Figure drawing* by Andrew Loomis to learn how to draw exaggerated muscles.
   D Everything in a comic, including minor details like planes, computers, and trees, must be drawn correctly.

8. **A** He can speak german.
   B His grandmother lives in Germany.
   C Does the flight arrive in Berlin, Germany on Tuesday afternoon?
   D Were East and West Germany reunified?

45

Practice 15: Edit for Capitalization

Recognize appropriate capitalization (II.C)

Directions: Read the sentences. Decide which sentence has a word that needs a capital letter.

1. **A** The abacus was an ancient calculator.
   B The chinese used it as early as 500 B.C.
   C Sophia, multiply those two numbers.
   D Mr. Conn's abacus had colored beads.

2. **A** The Web site "Welcome to the White House" provides a virtual tour of the White house.
   B Did you listen to the sound files of presidential speeches?
   C You can even send an e-mail to the president.
   D Where can I find a portrait of each U.S. president?

3. **A** I am interested in learning more about my Italian ancestry.
   B How is christmas celebrated in Italy?
   C My mom made a special Italian dish for Easter.
   D Some areas I would like to see are Rome, Lombardy, and Campania.

4. **A** Square dancing evolved from european folk dances.
   B Dances were held as a way to socialize with neighbors.
   C Western square dancing is still a popular way to socialize and exercise.
   D To square dance, all that was needed was a wooden floor, some music, and a caller.

5. **A** Jesse said, "I'm getting sleepy."
   B Why did Madison and I stay up so late?
   C We were watching T.V. and eating popcorn.
   D My mom implored, "clean up the living room."

6. **A** There are two kinds of sports injuries: overuse injuries and acute injuries.
   B Overuse injuries can cause stress fractures and muscle tears.
   C After puberty, boys are three times more likely than girls to get injured.
   D skaters most often injure their wrists and elbows.

7. **A** Initially, only a Pharaoh could afford mummification, as it was expensive.
   B Egyptians stopped making mummies when many became christians.
   C Estimates are that more than 70 million mummies were made in Egypt.
   D Egyptians were fascinated by the promise of eternal life.

8. **A** Dedicated to promoting science education, the museum is located in Philadelphia.
   B It was named in honor of the inventor Ben Franklin.
   C Ben Franklin created many useful inventions.
   D We toured the Franklin Institute science Museum.

Practice 16: Capitalization
Recognize appropriate capitalization (II.C)

Directions: Read the sentence. Decide which part needs a capital letter. Mark the letter for your answer.

1. The most | intriguing planet to me | has always been | neptune.
   Ⓐ   Ⓑ   Ⓒ   Ⓓ

2. Courtney's parents | have relatives | who live in | the Far east.
   Ⓐ   Ⓑ   Ⓒ   Ⓓ

3. Uncle tod's | dog Pip | was befriended by | a German shepherd.
   Ⓐ   Ⓑ   Ⓒ   Ⓓ

4. Julia received | a letter | of recommendation | from senator Snell.
   Ⓐ   Ⓑ   Ⓒ   Ⓓ

5. Does your | family always | celebrate easter at | your grandmother's house?
   Ⓐ   Ⓑ   Ⓒ   Ⓓ

6. I watched | the movie | *Field of dreams* | with Kelly and Jessica.
   Ⓐ   Ⓑ   Ⓒ   Ⓓ

Practice 17: Capitalization
Recognize appropriate capitalization (II.C)

Directions: Read the sentence. Decide which part needs a capital letter. Mark the letter for your answer.

1. Mr. and Mrs. Stinson | were amazed by the size | of the Great salt Lake | in Utah.
   Ⓐ   Ⓑ   Ⓒ   Ⓓ

2. Ralph Waldo Emerson said, | "the only way to have | a friend is | to be one."
   Ⓐ   Ⓑ   Ⓒ   Ⓓ

3. My mentor, Mr. Spitz, | is related to | mayor Paul Spitz | of Los Angeles.
   Ⓐ   Ⓑ   Ⓒ   Ⓓ

4. Danielle asked, | "Are you studying | about the time period | called the Middle ages?"
   Ⓐ   Ⓑ   Ⓒ   Ⓓ

5. My uncle just | purchased a new car; | it's a red | Pontiac sunbird.
   Ⓐ   Ⓑ   Ⓒ   Ⓓ

6. On Monday through Friday, | february 5-10, | we have a break | from Davis Middle School.
   Ⓐ   Ⓑ   Ⓒ   Ⓓ

Practice 18: Capitalization
Recognize appropriate capitalization (II.C)

Directions: Read the sentence. Decide which part needs a capital letter. Mark the letter for your answer.

1. I used to fish | at Woodlawn lake | every Wednesday | during the summer.
   Ⓐ   Ⓑ   Ⓒ   Ⓓ

2. Read the | novel by author | Jane Yolen entitled | *devil's Arithmetic.*
   Ⓐ   Ⓑ   Ⓒ   Ⓓ

3. I would love | to shop with Melissa | at the stores on Park avenue | in New York City.
   Ⓐ   Ⓑ   Ⓒ   Ⓓ

4. The best movie | that our english teacher | showed was | "Island of the Blue Dolphins."
   Ⓐ   Ⓑ   Ⓒ   Ⓓ

5. Did Spencer eat | an oscar Mayer hot dog | at the PTA picnic | last Saturday?
   Ⓐ   Ⓑ   Ⓒ   Ⓓ

6. We love mexican food, | especially tasty dishes | such as tacos | with rice and beans.
   Ⓐ   Ⓑ   Ⓒ   Ⓓ

Practice 19: Spelling, Capitalization, and Punctuation
Recognize appropriate spelling, capitalization, and punctuation (II.A-C)

Directions: Read each passage. Decide which type of mistake, if any, appears in each underlined section. Mark the letter for your answer.

Why are tropical fish so colorful? The <u>vibrant yellows, purples, whites oranges, and blues</u>

(1)
of tropical fish exist for all sorts of reasons. Some tropical fish are venomous. <u>Thier brilliant</u>

(2)
<u>colors</u> are an underwater billboard that signal to hungry fish that, if they want to live, they'd

better munch on something else.

Colors also serve as camouflage. Some species have a big black spot on the tail, called a

false eye spot. <u>This spot fools a Predator into</u> striking the wrong end of the animal, and the

(3)
swift fish gets away.

Adapted from The Ohio State University; College of Food, Agricultural and Environmental Sciences, 2000

---

1. A Spelling

   B Capitalization

   C Punctuation

   D No mistake

2. A Spelling

   B Capitalization

   C Punctuation

   D No mistake

3. A Spelling

   B Capitalization

   C Punctuation

   D No mistake

Practice 20: Spelling, Capitalization, and Punctuation

Recognize appropriate spelling, capitalization, and punctuation (II.A-C)

Directions: Read each passage. Decide which type of mistake, if any, appears in each underlined section. Mark the letter for your answer.

Dear Dr. Sandoval
_____
(1)

    I am interested in becoming a pediatrician. Could you please help me by answering a few

questions about this carear? First, what made you want to become a childrens doctor?
_____   _____
(2)   (3)

Second, what school subjects have been most helpful to you in your work as a pediatrician?

Last of all, what suggestions do you have for a student who wants to be a doctor? Thank you

for your time and I look forward to receiving your responses.

                         Sincerely,

                         Anita Luther

---

1. A Spelling

   B Capitalization

   C Punctuation

   D No mistake

2. A Spelling

   B Capitalization

   C Punctuation

   D No mistake

3. A Spelling

   B Capitalization

   C Punctuation

   D No mistake

Practice 21: Spelling, Capitalization, and Punctuation

Recognize appropriate spelling, capitalization, and punctuation (II.A-C)

Directions: Read each passage. Decide which type of mistake, if any, appears in each underlined section. Mark the letter for your answer.

One year, a brave little company of <u>people traveled across the plians</u> in big covered wagons
                                          (1)

with many horses, and finally succeeded in climbing to <u>the top of the rocky Mountains</u>. There
                                                              (2)

was a valley in the midst of the mountains. It was a valley <u>of brown bare desert soil</u> in a
                                                                  (3)

climate where almost no rain falls. The snow on the mountains, however, sent down little

streams of pure water. The winds were gentle, so the pioneers settled there.

Adapted from "The Gulls of Salt Lake"

---

1. **A** Spelling

   B Capitalization

   C Punctuation

   D No mistake

2. **A** Spelling

   B Capitalization

   C Punctuation

   D No mistake

3. **A** Spelling

   B Capitalization

   C Punctuation

   D No mistake

Practice 22: Capitalization and Punctuation
Recognize appropriate capitalization and punctuation (II.B,C)

Directions: Choose the answer that is written correctly and shows the correct capitalization and punctuation.

1. **A** Tara confessed, "I drank the last soda."
   B Jenny said, "That cola was mine Tara."
   C Who drank the last pop, Tara or Jenny.
   D "There are more drinks in the refrigerator" replied Edward.

2. **A** How beautiful the beaches are in Florida?
   B Dont forget to give me some money.
   C His Uncle dan drives a truck.
   D My uncle lives in Orlando, Florida.

3. **A** My parents both voted in the last election, didn't they.
   B He is the senator of new hampshire.
   C I attended a party hosted by Senator Timon.
   D His office is located on the corner of First street and Pine Avenue.

4. **A** Robert h. Schuller said, "Always look at what you have left. Never look at what you have lost."
   B "Always look at what you have left. Never look at what you have lost," said Robert H. Schuller.
   C Did Robert H. Schuller say, "Always look at what you have left. Never look at what you have lost."
   D Robert h. Schuller said, "Always look at what you have left? Never look at what you have lost."

5. **A** "Stir the brownie mix for 50 strokes" Martha reminded me.
   B "Stir the brownie mix for 50 strokes." Martha reminded me.
   C Stir the brownie mix for 50 strokes, Martha reminded me.
   D "Stir the brownie mix for 50 strokes," Martha reminded me.

6. **A** Isn't Katrinas watch fantastic?
   B Her watch is fantastic, isnt it?
   C Isn't Katrina's watch fantastic?
   D She purchased her fantastic watch at Rosedale mall.

Practice 23: Capitalization and Punctuation

Recognize appropriate capitalization and punctuation (II.B,C)

Directions: Choose the answer that is written correctly and shows the correct capitalization and punctuation.

1. **A** Will Autumn's book report about Anne frank earn her an A?

   B Autumn's book report about anne frank earned her an A.

   C Did Autumns book report about Anne Frank earn her an A!

   D Autumn's book report about Anne Frank earned her an A.

2. **A** This year we will study about slavery and the American revolution.

   B We will also research the clash of Native American and european cultures.

   C How did the Native American and European cultures clash?

   D What were the results of the american revolution?

3. **A** I like this chinese proverb: "Better to light a candle than to curse the darkness."

   B I like this Chinese proverb: "Better to light a candle than to curse the darkness."

   C I like this Chinese proverb Better to light a candle than to curse the darkness.

   D I like this Chinese proverb, "better to light a candle than to curse the darkness."

4. **A** Our generations problems include hunger disposal and energy use.

   B Our generation's problems include hunger, disposal, and energy use.

   C Our generations problems include: hunger disposal, and energy use.

   D Do our generations problems include hunger, disposal, and energy use.

5. **A** Why do kids get out of control on the school bus.

   B Principal Aliki said "Bus behavior can be very problematic."

   C According to Principal Aliki, bus behavior is a problem.

   D Some kids get out of control on the bus, don't they.

6. **A** Whenever we have group projects; kids argue and complain about fairness.

   B With group projects: Kid's complain and argue.

   C Too much complaining and arguing takes place among groups.

   D Did your group argue and complain.

54

Practice 24: Capitalization and Punctuation

Recognize appropriate capitalization and punctuation (II.B,C)

Directions: Choose the answer that is written correctly and shows the correct capitalization and punctuation.

1. **A** Peer pressure is about: music dress language and being "in or out."

   B School brings increased peer pressure about music, dress, language, and being "in or out."

   C Doesnt school bring increased peer pressure about music, dress, language, and being "in or out?"

   D School brings increased peer pressure about music dress, language, and being "in or out."

2. **A** My mom said, "Be respectful to others."

   B My Mom said "Be respectful to others.

   C My mom said be respectful to others.

   D My mom said, "be respectful to others."

3. **A** What is the difference between the terms "alternative sport" and "extreme sport."

   B Paul Vail, a BMX freestyle bike-rider, prefers the term "alternative sport" to "extreme sport"?

   C Paul Vail calls BMX bike riding an alternative sport.

   D bmx bike riding is considered an extreme sport by some.

4. **A** What do pre-teens collect.

   B Pre-teens collect: jewelry make-up, and music.

   C A pre-teen might collect jewelry, make-up, or music.

   D How many CDs do you have in your collection Pete?

5. **A** All organisms depend; on two main global food webs.

   B One includes ocean plants, the other includes land plants.

   C Ocean plants, does this group include microscopic plants and the animals that feed on them.

   D Organisms decompose they return food material to the environment.

6. **A** Roy Azdak said, "Good art is not what it looks like, but what it does to us."

   B Roy Azdak said good art is not what it looks like; but what it does to us.

   C Roy Azdak said that good art is not what it looks like. But what it does to us.

   D Roy Azdak said "good art is not what it looks like, but what it does to us."

Practice 25: Usage (Sentences)

Recognize standard grammar and usage (II.D)

Directions: Choose the word or group of words that *best* completes each sentence.

1. How many of _____ aluminum cans do you need to recycle?

   A this

   B these

   C them

   D thems

2. Miguel asked, "Are you and _____ still going to play baseball on Sunday?"

   A we

   B I

   C me

   D they

3. _____ both read the book *Bud, Not Buddy.*

   A Me and Marissa

   B Marissa and me

   C I and Marissa

   D Marissa and I

4. My mother refused to buy me the _____ expensive CD player the store carried.

   A mostest

   B most

   C more

   D moster

5. Nola, did you paint that picture all by _____?

   A yours

   B you

   C yourself

   D herself

6. We need four _____ of bread to make enough sandwiches for everyone.

   A loaf

   B loafes

   C loafs

   D loaves

Practice 26: Usage (Sentences)
Recognize standard grammar and usage (II.D)

Directions: Choose the word or group of words that *best* completes each sentence.

1. Our football team _____ worse seasons than this one.

   A has overcome
   B overcomed
   C overcoming
   D has been overcome

2. I rolled with one die; Shannon rolled with two _____

   A dies
   B dices
   C die
   D dice

3. Jesse whispered very _____, "Hush, my sister is still sleeping."

   A softest
   B softly
   C more soft
   D softer

4. Mary needed to get a library book from _____ locker.

   A us
   B she
   C her
   D herself

5. Claudio _____ behind a chair in the living room.

   A hid
   B hidden
   C hide
   D hiding

6. Although _____ are neighbors, we hardly see one another.

   A I and she
   B me and she
   C she and me
   D she and I

Practice 27: Usage (Sentences)
Recognize standard grammar and usage (II.D)

Directions: Choose the word or group of words that *best* completes each sentence.

1. How many _____ of coffee flavors Starbucks has!

   A varietys
   B variety
   C varieties
   D variety's

2. By next Thursday, you _____ an improvement in your appetite.

   A notice
   B will notice
   C noticed
   D are noticing

3. Yesterday, Mark _____ his baby photograph to the class; it was adorable.

   A shown
   B showing
   C show
   D showed

4. _____ and Madison are carpooling to school this year.

   A His
   B Us
   C Him
   D He

5. Will you share your markers with _____?

   A us
   B we
   C they
   D I

6. Joseph exclaimed, "Eating at Pizza Palace is a _____ dining experience!"

   A wonderfuler
   B wonderful
   C wonderfullest
   D most wonderfuler

Practice 28: Usage (Passage)

Recognize standard grammar and usage (II.D)

Directions: Read the passage. Choose the word or group of words that belongs in each space. Mark the letter for your answer.

> _____(1)_____ are always competing for the best science grades. There isn't _____(2)_____ who can make as many 100s as Michael. He is by far the _____(3)_____ boy in the sixth grade.

1. **A** I and he
   B He and I
   C He and me
   D Him and me

2. **A** nobody
   B anybody
   C not anyone
   D no one

3. **A** smart
   B most smarter
   C more smart
   D smartest

59

Practice 29: Usage (Passage)

Recognize standard grammar and usage (II.D)

Directions: Read the passage. Choose the word or group of words that belongs in each space. Mark the letter for your answer.

> This year, I would like to extend my bedtime by ____(1)____ hour, from 9 p.m. to 10 p.m. Alas, ____(2)____ my mom ____(3)____ my dad will agree.

1. **A** and
   B a
   C an
   D the

2. **A** not
   B none
   C either
   D neither

3. **A** nor
   B and
   C no
   D not

Practice 30: Usage (Passage)

Recognize standard grammar and usage (II.D)

Directions: Read the passage. Choose the word or group of words that belongs in each space. Mark the letter for your answer.

> I like to work crossword puzzles. This hobby ____(1)____ me to be a better speller. The word clues are riddles to solve. ____(2)____ are few hobbies that would be ____(3)____ to me. That's why I enjoy being a budding wordsmith.

1. **A** help
   B helps
   C helping
   D are helping

2. **A** They
   B Their
   C They're
   D There

3. **A** as challenging
   B challenge
   C challenger
   D more challenge

Practice 31: Grammar, Capitalization, Punctuation, and Spelling

Recognize correct spelling, punctuation, capitalization, and grammar (II.A-D)

Directions: Read the passage. Use the passage to answer the questions below it.

---

(1)The brooklyn bridge is a famous structure between Manhattan and Brooklyn in New York City. (2)Central Park is also locate in New York City. (3)Did you already know theses two facts?

---

1. In sentence 1, The brooklyn bridge is should be written—

    A The Brooklyn bridge
    B The brooklyn Bridge
    C The Brooklyn Bridge
    D No mistake

2. In sentence 2, is also locate in should be written—

    A is also located in
    B is also locating in
    C is also locates in
    D No mistake

3. In sentence 3, already know theses should be written—

    A already know thoses
    B already know these
    C already know this
    D No mistake

Practice 32: Grammar, Capitalization, Punctuation, and Spelling

Recognize correct spelling, punctuation, capitalization, and grammar (II.A-D)

Directions: Read the passage. Use the passage to answer the questions below it.

---

(1)It had taken months to <u>make the terible journey.</u> (2)Many had died of weariness and <u>illness on the way many had died</u> of hardship during the winter. (3)<u>By the Spring their provisions</u> were nearly gone, so they were living partly on roots dug from the ground. (4)All their lives now depended on the crops of grain and vegetables which they could raise in the valley.

Adapted from "The Gulls of Salt Lake"

---

1. In sentence 1, <u>make the terible journey</u> should be written—

   A make the tearible journey

   B make the terrable journey

   C make the terrible journey

   D No mistake

2. In sentence 2, <u>illness on the way many had died</u> should be written—

   A illness on the way: many had died

   B illness on the way; many had died

   C illness on the way? Many had died

   D No mistake

3. In sentence 3, <u>By the Spring their provisions</u> should be written—

   A By the spring their provisions

   B By the spring their Provisions

   C by the Spring their provisions

   D No mistake

Practice 33: Grammar, Capitalization, Punctuation, and Spelling

Recognize correct spelling, punctuation, capitalization, and grammar (II.A-D)

Directions: Read the poetry selection. Use the passage to answer the questions below it.

---

(1)The noise of Waters

by James Joyce

(2)All day I hear the noise of waters making moan,

(3)Sad as the seabird is, when going fourth alone,

(4)He hears the winds cry to the waters' monotone.

(5)The grey winds, the cold winds is blowing where I go.

(6)I hear the noise of many waters far below.

(7)All day, all night I hear them flowing to and fro.

---

1. In line 1, the title The noise of Waters should be written—

   A The noise of waters

   B The Noise of Waters

   C the noise of waters

   D No mistake

2. In line 3, when going fourth alone, should be written—

   A when going furth alone,

   B when going foarth alone,

   C when going forth alone,

   D No mistake

3. In line 5, the cold winds is blowing should be written—

   A the cold winds are blowing

   B the cold winds be blowing

   C the cold winds blowed

   D No mistake

Written Composition

III. Produce an effective composition for a specific purpose

A. Write for a variety of purposes and audiences

B. Use voice and style appropriate to audience and purpose

C. Use literary devices effectively (e.g., suspense, dialogue, figurative language)

D. Organize ideas, use effective transitions, choose precise wording

E. Demonstrate control of the English language (e.g., spelling, capitalization, usage)

F. Use complete sentences (e.g., simple, complex, declarative, imperative)

G. Employ editing strategies (e.g., elaboration, deletion, and rearrangement of words)

H. Revise drafts for coherence, progression, and logical support of ideas

Notes

Types of Writing
Written Composition (III.A-H)

Most states require students to write a composition as part of their English Language Arts/Writing Test. This section includes descriptions of different types of writing. It also includes a description of successful responses for each type of writing, and several writing prompts for student compositions.

States vary in their expectations for compositions. Some are required to be final rather than first drafts. Teachers can use the rubrics on pages 120-122 to score student compositions. Teachers can also score student writing according to their states' expectations or their own criteria.

The Teaching Strategies section on pages 113-119 contains helpful strategies for teaching audience, elaboration, control of language, and more.

The following are descriptions of writing tasks commonly given to sixth-grade students.

Description

Write a composition to describe an object, person, place, situation, or picture.

Narration

Write a narrative (story) on a specified topic.

Directions

Write a composition to tell how to do something.

Compare/Contrast

Write a composition in which ideas/objects/people/places are classified according to specified criteria and described.

Persuasion

Write a composition in which you make a choice and support the choice with convincing reasons.

Notes

Description

Practices 1-6

Writing Task: Write a composition to describe an object, person, place, situation, or picture.

The successful composition will—

- be specific and elaborated

- include figurative language and/or rich detail

- remain on topic from beginning to end

- paint a vivid picture of an object or scene with picturesque words and/or sophisticated sentence structure

- describe a lengthy set of features

- be consistent in organizational strategy

- not digress into an expressive/ narrative composition

Reproduce the bookmarks on the right as a reminder for each of your students.

Description

Writing Task: Write a composition to describe an object, person, place, situation, or picture.

I need to:

★ Use words to paint a picture of the object/scene

★ Describe one thing at a time

★ Organize my details

Description

Writing Task: Write a composition to describe an object, person, place, situation, or picture.

I need to:

★ Use words to paint a picture of the object/scene

★ Describe one thing at a time

★ Organize my details

Adapted from TAAS MASTER Writing by Lori Mammen, ECS Learning Systems, Inc.

Practice 1

Description

Think of the most interesting person that you know. Who is it and what makes this person so interesting? Describe this person in detail.

_____

(title)

_____

_____

_____

_____

_____

_____

_____

_____

_____

_____

_____

_____

_____

Practice 2

Description

I absolutely love...

Describe something that you love. It could be a food dish, a hobby, a person—anything. Describe what you love and include specific details.

(title)

Practice 3

Description

Describe an assignment that you particularly enjoyed. Describe your assignment in detail.

_____
(title)

_____

_____

_____

_____

_____

_____

_____

_____

_____

_____

_____

_____

_____

_____

Practice 4

Description

Think of a celebration you attended, such as a birthday party, where you had lots of fun. Describe the celebration and what made it so enjoyable for you.

_____

(title)

_____

_____

_____

_____

_____

_____

_____

_____

_____

_____

_____

_____

_____

_____

_____

_____

_____

_____

Practice 5

Description

Unfortunately, we all have bad days. Describe the absolute worst day of your life. Be sure to include specific details.

_____

(title)

_____

_____

_____

_____

_____

_____

_____

_____

_____

_____

_____

_____

_____

©ECS Learning Systems, Inc.

74

Practice 6

Description

Describe the ways that you have changed as you have become older. What is different about your appearance and behavior? What is still the same?

_____

(title)

_____

_____

_____

_____

_____

_____

_____

_____

_____

_____

_____

_____

_____

_____

_____

_____

Notes

Narration
Practices 7-12

Writing Task: Write a narrative (story) on a specified topic.

The successful composition will—

- present ideas in chronological order; sequence events

- use transitions

- show a progression through time

- develop a beginning, middle, and end

- include aspects of characterization, setting, and plot

- resolve the action/problem

Reproduce the bookmarks on the right as a reminder for each of your students.

Narration	**Narration**
Writing Task: Write a narrative (story) on a specified topic.	Writing Task: Write a narrative (story) on a specified topic.

I need to:

★ Write a story that explains
- who
- what
- where
- when
- why

★ Develop a beginning, middle, and end for my story

★ Start in a way that "hooks" the reader

★ Have an exciting or strong ending to my story

★ Use words that make my story come alive

I need to:

★ Write a story that explains
- who
- what
- where
- when
- why

★ Develop a beginning, middle, and end for my story

★ Start in a way that "hooks" the reader

★ Have an exciting or strong ending to my story

★ Use words that make my story come alive

Adapted from TAAS MASTER Writing *by Lori Mammen, ECS Learning Systems, Inc.*

Practice 7
Narration

Something unexpected happens on your way to school. Write a story about what happens.

_____
(title)

_____

_____

_____

_____

_____

_____

_____

_____

_____

_____

_____

_____

_____

Practice 8

Narration

Imagine that you have created a product that everyone wants. Write a story telling about your hot product and how being its inventor has changed your life. Be sure to use specific details.

_____

(title)

_____

_____

_____

_____

_____

_____

_____

_____

_____

_____

_____

_____

_____

Practice 9

Narration

"The printer chewed up my paper..."

Tell a story about what happened to your homework assignment. Be sure to write about your story in detail.

_____

(title)

Practice 10
Narration

The school cafeteria suddenly became noisy with the sound of trays banging... **Continue this story by telling what happened in the school cafeteria.**

_____
(title)

_____

_____

_____

_____

_____

_____

_____

_____

_____

_____

_____

_____

_____

_____

Practice 11
Narration

Imagine that you are asked to speak with the school principal. What is the reason for your meeting? Write a story about what happens. Be sure to use specific details.

(title)

_____

_____

_____

_____

_____

_____

_____

_____

_____

_____

_____

_____

_____

_____

_____

Practice 12

Narration

Fear is an emotion that most people have experienced at one time or another. Write a story that deals with fear. The situation can be real or imaginary.

(title)

_____

_____

_____

_____

_____

_____

_____

_____

_____

_____

_____

_____

_____

Notes

Directions
Practices 13-18

Writing Task: Write a composition telling how to do something.

The successful composition will—

- delineate steps needed to complete a specified task

- be unambiguous, specific, and elaborated

- order steps sequentially

- be consistent in organizational strategy

Reproduce the bookmarks on the right as a reminder for each of your students.

Directions

Writing Task: Write a composition telling how to do something.

I need to:

- Give all the steps for completing the task
- Write the steps for my directions in order
- Organize my directions carefully
- Give clear directions by using the best words I can
- Help the reader by using transitional words like: first, second, next, finally, soon, later on, and afterwards

Directions

Writing Task: Write a composition telling how to do something.

I need to:

- Give all the steps for completing the task
- Write the steps for my directions in order
- Organize my directions carefully
- Give clear directions by using the best words I can
- Help the reader by using transitional words like: first, second, next, finally, soon, later on, and afterwards

Adapted from TAAS MASTER Writing *by Lori Mammen, ECS Learning Systems, Inc.*

Practice 13

Directions

Your friend has invited you on a hiking trip. Explain how to pack for your hiking trip. What do you do first? Then what do you do? Tell all the steps in order.

_____

(title)

_____

_____

_____

_____

_____

_____

_____

_____

_____

_____

_____

_____

_____

_____

Practice 14
Directions

Write directions for how to train as an athlete for a particular sport. Name the sport. What do you do first? Then what do you do?

_____
(title)
_____

_____

_____

_____

_____

_____

_____

_____

_____

_____

_____

_____

_____

_____

Practice 15

Directions

Think about how to recycle an item you would normally throw away. Examples are an empty box or an old appliance. Write directions for how to create something from your recycled item. What materials do you need for this project? What would you do first? Give all the steps for creating your project.

_____

(title)

_____

_____

_____

_____

_____

_____

_____

_____

_____

_____

_____

_____

_____

_____

Practice 16

Directions

How would you plan the ultimate birthday surprise for someone you care about? Write a composition telling a classmate how to plan the ultimate birthday surprise. What things do you need? Explain each step fully so that a classmate would know how to duplicate your birthday surprise.

_____
(title)

_____

_____

_____

_____

_____

_____

_____

_____

_____

_____

_____

_____

_____

Practice 17
Directions

Create directions for how to have a really wonderful day. Explain each step fully so that someone else could follow your directions.

_____
(title)

_____

_____

_____

_____

_____

_____

_____

_____

_____

_____

_____

_____

_____

_____

Practice 18

Directions

Write directions for creating the perfect place to hang out at with your friends. It could be a clubhouse or a room in your house. Where is it located? What is inside of it? Be specific so that someone else could follow your directions.

_____

(title)

_____

_____

_____

_____

_____

_____

_____

_____

_____

_____

_____

_____

_____

_____

_____

Notes

Compare/Contrast

Practices 19-24

Writing Task: Write a composition in which ideas/objects/people/ places are classified according to specified criteria and described.

The successful composition will—

- be consistent in organizational strategy

- remain on topic from beginning to end

- include specific and elaborated information about ideas/objects/people/places

- delineate relationships between ideas

- classify specified ideas/objects/people/places in a logical way

Reproduce the bookmarks on the right as a reminder for each of your students.

Compare/Contrast

Writing Task: To compare/contrast ideas, objects, people, or places.

I need to:

- Stay on topic from beginning to end

- Support my central idea with specific information and examples

- Show how things are alike/different, good/bad, or other according to the writing prompt

- Organize my ideas logically

Compare/Contrast

Writing Task: To compare/contrast ideas, objects, people, or places.

I need to:

- Stay on topic from beginning to end

- Support my central idea with specific information and examples

- Show how things are alike/different, good/bad, or other according to the writing prompt

- Organize my ideas logically

Adapted from TAAS MASTER Writing *by Lori Mammen, ECS Learning Systems, Inc.*

Practice 19
Compare/Contrast

Think about your school schedule. What if your most difficult subject was scheduled first? Write a composition describing the *advantages* and *disadvantages* of having your most difficult subject first during the day. Write about your ideas in detail.

_____
(title)

_____

_____

_____

_____

_____

_____

_____

_____

_____

_____

_____

_____

_____

Practice 20
Compare/Contrast

You invited eight friends to your house, and they all accepted your invitation! Write a letter to your parents explaining *both* what is *good* and what is *bad* about having eight friends at your house at the same time. Be sure to explain each point fully.

_____

Practice 21

Compare/Contrast

Your school has decided to conduct backpack checks in which the contents of student backpacks are searched. Write a composition for your principal identifying *both* the *advantages* and *disadvantages* of backpack checks. Be sure to write about your ideas in detail.

_____
(title)

_____

_____

_____

_____

_____

_____

_____

_____

_____

_____

_____

_____

_____

Practice 22

Compare/Contrast

Your parents have decided that you should participate in an extracurricular activity after school, such as band or sports. Write a letter to your parents explaining what you would *like* and what you *wouldn't like* about being involved in an extracurricular activity after school. Be sure to explain each point fully.

_____
(title)

_____

_____

_____

_____

_____

_____

_____

_____

_____

_____

_____

_____

_____

Practice 23
Compare/Contrast

Overnight, you have become the smartest kid in the world. Write a letter to your friend explaining *both* **the** *advantages* **and the** *disadvantages* **of being the smartest kid in the world. Be sure to write about your ideas in detail.**

_____

_____

_____

_____

_____

_____

_____

_____

_____

_____

_____

_____

_____

_____

_____

_____

_____

Practice 24
Compare/Contrast

Imagine what life will be like when you are an adult. Write a detailed composition for your teacher explaining *both* what will be *good* and what will be *bad* about being an adult.

_____

(title)

_____

_____

_____

_____

_____

_____

_____

_____

_____

_____

_____

_____

_____

_____

Notes

Persuasion

Practices 25-30

Writing Task: Write a composition in which you make a choice and support the choice with convincing reasons.

The successful composition will—

- contain a clear sense of order and completeness

- be characterized by overall fluency of expression

- include effective use of transitional, introductory, and concluding elements

- contain highly effective word choice

- have an apparent persuasive tone

- contain sufficient elaboration of reasons to make them understood and convincing

Reproduce the bookmarks on the right as a reminder for each of your students.

Persuasion

Writing Task: Write a composition supporting a particular point of view.

I need to:

- Take a stand on an issue

- Support my statements with convincing arguments

- Explain each argument fully

- Organize my ideas logically

Persuasion

Writing Task: Write a composition supporting a particular point of view.

I need to:

- Take a stand on an issue

- Support my statements with convincing arguments

- Explain each argument fully

- Organize my ideas logically

Adapted from TAAS MASTER Writing by Lori Mammen, ECS Learning Systems, Inc.

Practice 25
Persuasion

What do you think should be done to keep people who are under the influence of alcohol from driving? Write a letter to your state representative persuading him or her to consider your proposal. Be sure to explain in detail your plan for keeping drunk drivers off the road.

Practice 26
Persuasion

Which quality is most important to you in a friend: loyalty, honesty, or generosity? Choose only one quality that is most important to you, and write a persuasive essay. Be sure to give convincing reasons for your choice.

_____
(title)

_____

_____

_____

_____

_____

_____

_____

_____

_____

_____

_____

_____

_____

_____

Practice 27
Persuasion

Does watching violence on television and in video games have a positive or negative effect on young people? Write a composition persuading your teacher about the effect that watching violence has on young people. Use convincing details to support your opinion.

_____
(title)

_____

_____

_____

_____

_____

_____

_____

_____

_____

_____

_____

_____

_____

_____

_____

Practice 28
Persuasion

Which grade level has been the most fun for you? Write a letter to your friend persuading him/her that the grade level you select has been the most fun. Be sure to explain your reasons in detail.

Practice 29

Persuasion

Is it ever all right to lie? Why, or why not?

_____
(title)

_____

_____

_____

_____

_____

_____

_____

_____

_____

_____

_____

_____

_____

_____

Practice 30
Persuasion

Three of your teachers have decided to give exams on the same day. Persuade your teachers to change their test schedules by suggesting an alternative. Give convincing reasons why your plan would be better for students than having three tests on one day.

_____
(title)

_____

_____

_____

_____

_____

_____

_____

_____

_____

_____

_____

_____

_____

Notes

Appendix

- Answer Keys

- Teaching Strategies

- Scoring Rubrics for Compositions

- Checklists for Student Writers

- Answer Sheet

Answer Key: Sentence Structure

Practice 1 (p. 13)

1. D   2. B   3. C   4. C   5. D

6. C   7. A   8. C

Practice 2 (p. 14)

1. C   2. D   3. B   4. D   5. C

6. A   7. B   8. C

Practice 3 (p. 15)

1. A   2. C   3. B   4. C   5. D

6. D   7. C   8. A

Practice 4 (p. 16)

1. C   2. C   3. A

Practice 5 (p. 17)

1. B   2. A   3. C

Practice 6 (p. 18)

1. B   2. D   3. B

Practice 7 (p. 19)

1. B   2. C

Practice 8 (p. 20)

1. B   2. A

Practice 9 (p. 21)

1. B   2. C

Practice 10 (p. 22)

1. A   2. C

Practice 11 (p. 23)

1. C   2. B

Practice 12 (p. 24)

1. C   2. B

Practice 13 (p. 25)

1. D   2. C   3. B   4. D

Practice 14 (p. 26)

1. B   2. C   3. D   4. A

Practice 15 (p. 27)

1. A   2. D   3. D   4. B

Practice 16 (p. 28)

1. C   2. D   3. C

Practice 17 (p. 29)

1. A   2. C   3. D

Practice 18 (p. 30)

1. B   2. D   3. A

Answer Key: Standard Usage

Practice 1 (p. 32)

1. C 2. D 3. B 4. B 5. D
6. A

Practice 2 (p. 33)

1. C 2. C 3. B 4. A 5. D
6. A

Practice 3 (p. 34)

1. C 2. B 3. D 4. B 5. C
6. D

Practice 4 (p. 35)

1. A 2. B 3. A 4. D 5. A
6. B

Practice 5 (p. 36)

1. D 2. B 3. D 4. A 5. A
6. D

Practice 6 (p. 37)

1. A 2. B 3. A 4. B 5. B
6. C

Practice 7 (p. 38)

1. D 2. A 3. D 4. D 5. A
6. C

Practice 8 (p. 39)

1. B 2. D 3. D 4. B 5. C
6. D

Practice 9 (p. 40)

1. D 2. A 3. C 4. A 5. B
6. B

Practice 10 (p. 41)

1. A 2. B 3. D 4. C 5. C
6. B 7. D 8. B

Practice 11 (p. 42)

1. C 2. C 3. C 4. A 5. A
6. B 7. D 8. D

Practice 12 (p. 43)

1. A 2. D 3. B 4. D 5. C
6. C 7. B 8. C

Practice 13 (p. 44)

1. A 2. D 3. B 4. C 5. D
6. B 7. A 8. B

Practice 14 (p. 45)

1. D 2. B 3. C 4. C 5. A
6. D 7. C 8. A

Practice 15 (p. 46)

1. B 2. A 3. B 4. A 5. D
6. D 7. B 8. D

Practice 16 (p. 47)

1. D   2. D   3. A   4. D   5. C
6. C

Practice 17 (p. 48)

1. C   2. B   3. C   4. D   5. D
6. B

Practice 18 (p. 49)

1. B   2. D   3. C   4. B   5. B
6. A

Practice 19 (p. 50)

1. C   2. A   3. B

Practice 20 (p. 51)

1. C   2. A   3. C

Practice 21 (p. 52)

1. A   2. B   3. C

Practice 22 (p. 53)

1. A   2. D   3. C   4. B   5. D
6. C

Practice 23 (p. 54)

1. D   2. C   3. B   4. B   5. C
6. C

Practice 24 (p. 55)

1. B   2. A   3. C   4. C   5. B
6. A

Practice 25 (p. 56)

1. B   2. B   3. D   4. B   5. C
6. D

Practice 26 (p. 57)

1. A   2. D   3. B   4. C   5. A
6. D

Practice 27 (p. 58)

1. C   2. B   3. D   4. D   5. A
6. B

Practice 28 (p. 59)

1. B   2. B   3. D

Practice 29 (p. 60)

1. C   2. D   3. A

Practice 30 (p. 61)

1. B   2. D   3. A

Practice 31 (p. 62)

1. C   2. A   3. B

Practice 32 (p. 63)

1. C   2. B   3. A

Practice 33 (p. 64)

1. B   2. C   3. A

Tips for Teaching Types of Writing Tasks

Use these strategies to help students understand that there are different types of writing tasks.

- Identify the types of writing in textbooks, magazines, stories, and other literature. Is it a narrative, how to, or descriptive piece?

- Use a reading selection to discuss style, word choice, and organization. How do the author's choices relate to his/her purpose for writing?

- Designate one week as "Descriptive Writing Week" (or any other writing category you are emphasizing). Everyone brings in descriptive pieces of writing from magazines, newspapers, and books. What do these samples have in common? How are they different?

- Select a topic, such as "Exploring Space," for student writing. Write about exploring space for different purposes. For example, first describe how we currently explore space, then write a fantasy story about it. How are the two compositions different? How are they alike?

- Take a section from a student textbook, such as science. Rewrite it for a different purpose. For example, read information about forests, then write a description of what a forest looks and smells like.

- Select one of the writing tasks from this book. Identify the type of writing it requires. Maybe it is to write a story about an animal. Discuss how the writing would change if the purpose is to describe the animal.

Tips for Teaching Audience

Use these strategies to help students write appropriately for a wide range of readers.

• Before writing, always have the student ask: Who am I writing this for—myself? someone I know? someone I don't know?

• Remember, young authors are used to writing for the teacher or for themselves— students are usually their own audience. Give assignments that address a variety of audiences, especially for traditional types of writing. For example, have students write directions for another student to follow, rather than the teacher.

• Together, brainstorm a list of formal audiences, such as the school principal or a government official. Informal audiences include friends and family members.

• Provide a situation for student writing, such as failing a math test. Write about the topic for two different audiences. How does the audience determine language and tone?

Example: Write two letters, each explaining your failing grade on a math test.

Letter 1
Write the letter to your parents or grandparents.

Letter 2
Write the letter to your friend.

• Have students rewrite a textbook selection for a younger or older reader. Compare and contrast student writing to the textbook.

• Students can retell a well-known story for a different audience. For example, rewrite "The Three Little Pigs" for a group of wolves. How does the story change?

• Let students write letters to various people: movie and music stars, newspaper editors, friends, relatives, business people. How do the letters differ according to audience?

Helping Students Add Details to Writing

Elaboration is the effective use of specific details in writing. Students need to communicate clearly and precisely throughout their compositions. Accomplishing this involves two steps.

Step 1

Students select the most appropriate details and supporting ideas to include in their writing. Including extraneous information— "padding" with unnecessary details—often confuses or distracts the reader. Padding works against the goal of effective communication.

Step 2

Students arrange the details to enhance their reader's understanding. Writers should avoid simply stringing together a list of details. Instead, the details and supporting ideas should be thoughtfully arranged to help the reader grasp the writer's intentions.

Here are a variety of elaboration techniques, with definitions and examples. Teach students about these methods and how to apply them to their own compositions.

Action Word

Action words express an act or an event. Action words can add detail to writing when they are specific and exact.

Example: The couple *moved* across the dance floor and *went* out the door.

Elaborated Example: The couple *swept* across the dance floor and *glided* out the door.

Adjective

Adjectives modify nouns. When used effectively, adjectives can add detail, sensory impressions, and a richness to writing.

Example: He wore a suit and hat.

Elaborated Example: He wore an *old, tattered* suit and a *wide-brimmed cowboy* hat.

Adverb

Adverbs modify verbs, adjectives, and other adverbs. When used effectively, adverbs can add detail, sensory impressions, and a richness to writing.

Example: She walked down the street.

Elaborated Example: She walked *aimlessly* down the street.

Allusion

An allusion is an indirect reference to a character, event, or situation from another piece of literature. Allusions help create a vivid image for the reader.

Example: He used a lot of effort to complete the task.

Elaborated Example: He worked like Hercules to complete the task.

Analogy

Analogies are comparisons of two sets of ideas, items, or situations that are considered otherwise dissimilar. Like other kinds of comparisons, analogies help the reader create a more complete picture of the topic or idea discussed in the writing.

Example: His ideas started the whole project.

Elaborated Example: Just as a plant springs from a seed, the class project grew from his excellent idea.

Characterization

Characterization is the description or representation of a person's qualities or peculiarities. Effective characterization makes the character of a story or the piece of writing more life-like for the reader.

Example: She was a wicked old witch.

Elaborated Example: She was a wicked old witch who took delight in hearing the screams of terror when an unsuspecting child came too near.

Comparison/Contrast

Comparison and contrast draw attention to the similarities and differences between two or more items, people, or situations. Comparison and contrast can help create a complete picture in a piece of writing.

Example: The dog had a big bone.

Elaborated Example: The dog had a bone that seemed too large for his food dish.

Conversation

Conversation is the exchange of ideas, feelings, or opinions between two or more people or characters. Conversation adds a richness to writing because it goes beyond the simple recording of information and shows the involvement of characters or other individuals.

Example: My mother said I couldn't go.

Elaborated Example: My mother said, "I certainly will not allow you to go to that party."

Definition

A definition is a statement of the meaning of a word, phrase, or term. Accurate definitions make writing more specific.

Example: In class we are studying different kinds of trees.

Elaborated Example: In class we are studying different kinds of trees. The first type of tree we studied was the deciduous tree. Deciduous trees shed or lose their foliage at the end of the growing season.

Description

Description helps create a mental picture for the reader. Effective description is exact and specific and helps recreate an experience for the reader.

Example: The girl wore a dress.

Elaborated Example: The girl wore a red dress that fit loosely around her and touched the floor as she walked.

Detail

Details are the small and distinct pieces of information that add support and substance to a piece of writing.

Example: It looked like an alien.

Elaborated Example: It had huge, red antennae and green, lumpy skin.

Exaggeration

An exaggeration is an extravagant statement made about an object, idea, or situation. An exaggeration attracts the reader's attention, through deliberate overstatement or understatement. Deliberate exaggeration in writing is called hyperbole.

Example: Before his diet he weighed a lot.

Elaborated Example: Before his diet he weighed as much as an elephant.

Example

Examples provide instances that prove or support an idea. By using examples, the writer can expand or clarify an idea, statement, or opinion.

Example: Many of my friends are involved in sports.

Elaborated Example: Many of my friends are involved in sports. Just yesterday, Tony told me about his last tennis match.

Fact

Facts are accurate pieces of information used to support an idea or claim. Facts help the writer prove a point made in a piece of writing.

Example: Many students in this school need tutoring.

Elaborated Example: Since one out of three students earned a failing grade in an academic subject, many of them will need tutoring.

Location

Location specifies the exact place or situation of an object, person, or place. Location helps create a visual image for reader.

Example: The clock was on the table.

Elaborated Example: The clock rested behind some books at the back of the table.

Metaphor

A metaphor is a figure of speech that implies a similarity between two unlike objects by saying one object is actually another, or by giving one object the characteristics of the other. Metaphors add a richness to writing, making it come "alive."

Example: The boy was mean in the morning.

Elaborated Example: The boy growled at everyone in the morning.

Personal Anecdote

A personal anecdote is a brief story from the writer's life that adds information to a piece of writing. Such anecdotes add meaning and a personal touch to a composition.

Example: New friends have been important in my life.

Elaborated Example: New friends have been important in my life. I met Cindy on the first day of school. She helped me find my way around and feel at home in a new place.

Personification

Personification is a technique that gives an inanimate object some life-like characteristic. Personification makes writing more interesting.

Example: The trees made noises in the wind.

Elaborated Example: The trees moaned as the wind beat against them.

Quotation

A quotation is a statement of another person. Quotations can be used to expand on an idea.

Example: People who are alike often stay near one another.

Elaborated Example: People who are alike often stay near each other. This is a perfect example of the old saying "Birds of a feather flock together."

Sensory Image

The use of sensory details greatly enhances a piece of writing and helps the reader create a complete image from the writing.

Example: The smell was horrible.

Elaborated Example: She could smell the horrible odor of acrid smoke throughout the house.

Simile

This is another way of comparing two unlike people, objects, or situations. In this type of comparison, the comparison is made by using the words "as" or "like." Similes make writing more interesting and descriptive.

Example: I have a good friend who makes me happy.

Elaborated Example: When I am with my friend, I am as happy as a kid on the last day of school.

Superlative

Superlatives state descriptions to the highest degree. They add depth and emphasis to writing.

Example: The man's new car was fast.

Elaborated Example: The man's new car was the speediest car on the block.

Tips for Teaching the Use of Details

Use these strategies to help students effectively use specific details in their writing.

- Identify the elaboration strategies most appropriate for your students using the list on pages 115-118.

- Write an unelaborated sentence on the chalkboard or overhead projector. Try choosing an example from student writing. Students write an elaborated version of the sentence on paper. The method of elaboration can be specified.

Example

Unelaborated Sentence
The boy walked down the street.

Method of Elaboration
Metaphor

Directions
Improve this sentence by using a metaphor.

- Have students share their rewrites aloud. How are the new versions more effective than the original?

- Write an unelaborated sentence on the chalkboard or overhead projector. Divide the class into several sections. Direct each section to rewrite/elaborate in a different way. Students share their writing. Are the new sentences livelier than the originals?

- Together, brainstorm elaboration ideas for each writing task, before students begin writing. List their ideas on the chalkboard or overhead projector. Students select three to four techniques they will try to include in their writing. Revision and peer editing groups can focus on the success the students had in meeting their goals.

- Select three to four elaboration strategies for the age and ability level of your students, and for a particular writing task they have completed. Conduct a revision session. Have students focus on revising their work to include these elaboration techniques where appropriate.

Adapted from TAAS MASTER Writing *by Lori Mammen, ECS Learning Systems, Inc.*

Scoring Rubrics for Written Compositions

In most states that administer tests requiring student-written compositions, evaluators use scoring rubrics to assess these compositions. A scoring rubric is an assessment tool designed to determine the degree to which a writer meets the established criteria for a given writing task.

Many scoring rubrics allow for holistic evaluation, which focuses on the overall effectiveness of the written response rather than individual errors in content, organization, mechanics, etc. For example, a scoring rubric might allow a teacher to score papers on a scale from 1 (for the least effective responses) to 4 (for the most effective responses). Rubrics that offer a broader scale of points (e.g., 1–6) allow for a more refined evaluation of an essay. For example, with these rubrics it is possible for evaluators to distinguish between an outstanding response (e.g., 6) and a very good response (e.g., 5). Rubrics with a narrow scale of points (e.g., 0–2) do not allow for a very refined evaluation, generally limiting evaluators to a response of either "pass" or "fail."

Sample scoring rubrics appear on the following pages. They offer several options for evaluating the written compositions students complete for the writing prompts in *TestSMART*™. A brief description of each rubric follows.

Note: Teachers may also use scoring rubrics provided for their own state's competency test.

Four-point rubric
This rubric provides a four-point scale, making a somewhat refined evaluation possible. It does not, however, allow teachers to make clear distinctions between outstanding compositions and those that are merely good. The four-point rubric is appropriate for brief written responses (two to four sentences) and longer responses (two or more paragraphs).

Six-point rubric
Because of the broad scale of points, this rubric allows for a more refined evaluation of a written response. The six-point rubric is appropriate for longer responses (two or more paragraphs).

Scoring Rubric for Written Compositions

Four-Point Rubric

4
- Stays focused on topic throughout composition
- Includes thorough, complete ideas/information
- Follows clear, consistent organizational pattern
- Exhibits exceptional word usage and rich details
- Is fluent and easy to read
- Displays a strong sense of audience
- May include creative writing techniques

3
- Stays focused on topic throughout composition
- Includes many relevant ideas/pieces of information
- Has clear, consistent organizational pattern
- Exhibits more than adequate word usage
- Is fluent and easy to read
- Displays a sense of audience

2
- Stays somewhat focused on topic
- Includes some relevant ideas/pieces of information
- Has some clear, consistent organizational pattern
- Exhibits some adequate word usage
- Is readable
- Displays some sense of audience

1
- Exhibits less than minimal focus on topic
- Includes few relevant ideas and little information
- Has no clear, consistent organizational pattern
- Exhibits less than adequate word usage
- Is difficult to read
- Displays little sense of audience
- Note: Include here compositions which are inappropriate due to content (e.g., the writer advocates inappropriate actions, uses inappropriate language, or presents views blatantly contrary to general school policy)

Scoring Rubric for Written Compositions

Six-Point Rubric

6
Stays focused on topic throughout composition
Includes thorough, complete ideas/information
Follows clear, consistent organizational pattern
Exhibits exceptional word usage and rich details
Is fluent and easy to read
Displays a strong sense of audience
May include creative writing techniques

5
Stays focused on topic throughout composition
Includes many relevant ideas/pieces of information
Has clear, consistent organizational pattern
Exhibits more than adequate word usage
Is fluent and easy to read
Displays a sense of audience

4
Stays mostly focused on topic
Includes some relevant ideas/pieces of information
Has clear, consistent organizational pattern
Exhibits adequate word usage
Is readable
Displays some sense of audience

3
Stays somewhat focused on topic
Includes some relevant ideas and information
Has some consistent organizational pattern
Exhibits minimally adequate word usage
Is mostly readable
Displays some sense of audience

2
Exhibits less than minimal focus on topic
Includes few relevant ideas and little information
Has inconsistent organizational pattern
Exhibits less than adequate word usage
Is difficult to read
Displays little sense of audience
Note: Include here compositions which are inappropriate due to content
(e.g., the writer advocates inappropriate actions, uses inappropriate
language, or presents views blatantly contrary to general school
policy)

1
Has no focus on topic
Includes almost no relevant ideas or information
Has no order
Exhibits less than adequate word usage
Is illegible or incoherent
Displays no sense of audience
Is a blank paper
Is written entirely in a language other than English

Checklist for Student Writers
Description

I will earn my best score with a *descriptive* writing task if:

☐ I use my words to paint a picture of the object or scene.

☐ I stay on my topic from beginning to end.

☐ I describe one thing at a time.

☐ I organize my details.

☐ I use the best words in my descriptions, so my descriptions "sparkle."

☐ I help the reader by using transitional words like: first, second, next, finally, soon, later on, and afterwards.

☐ I use some of the ideas for describing things that I have learned.

I edit my writing for the correct use of:

☐ spelling

☐ grammar

☐ capitalization

☐ punctuation

Checklist for Student Writers
Narration

I will earn my best score with a *narrative* writing task if:

☐ My made-up story gives the names of the main characters.

☐ My story has a beginning, middle, and end.

☐ My story starts in a way that "hooks" the reader.

My story explains:

☐ who

☐ what

☐ where/when

☐ why

☐ I use words that make my story come alive; I do not use the same words over and over.

☐ I have an exciting/strong ending to my story.

I edit my writing for the correct use of:

☐ spelling

☐ grammar

☐ capitalization

☐ punctuation

Checklist for Student Writers

Directions

I will earn my best score with a *directions* writing task if:

☐ I give all the steps for how to do something.

☐ I put my steps in order from beginning to end.

☐ I explain each step in detail, well enough that someone could follow my directions.

☐ I give clear directions by using the best words I can.

☐ I help the reader by using transitional words like: first, second, next, finally, soon, later on, and afterwards.

I edit my writing for the correct use of:

☐ spelling

☐ grammar

☐ capitalization

☐ punctuation

Checklist for Student Writers
Compare/Contrast

I will earn my best score with a *compare/contrast* writing task if:

☐ I organize my ideas in a logical manner.

☐ I stay on my topic from beginning to end.

☐ I support my central idea with specific information and examples.

☐ I classify things according to the writing prompt, showing how ideas/people/objects/places are: alike or different, good or bad.

☐ I help the reader by using transitional words like: first, second, next, finally, soon, later on, and afterwards.

I edit my writing for the correct use of:

☐ spelling

☐ grammar

☐ capitalization

☐ punctuation

126

Checklist for Student Writers

Persuasion

I will earn my best score with a *persuasive* writing task if:

☐ I organize my ideas in a logical manner.

☐ I stay on my topic from beginning to end.

☐ I take a stand on an issue.

☐ I support all of my statements with convincing arguments.

☐ I explain each of my arguments fully.

☐ I use highly persuasive language.

☐ I help the reader by using transitional words like: first, second, next, finally, soon, later on, and afterwards.

I edit my writing for the correct use of:

☐ spelling

☐ grammar

☐ capitalization

☐ punctuation

Name _____   Date _____

Answer Sheet

Sentence Structure: Practice # _____

Standard Usage: Practice # _____

1. Ⓐ Ⓑ Ⓒ Ⓓ
2. Ⓐ Ⓑ Ⓒ Ⓓ
3. Ⓐ Ⓑ Ⓒ Ⓓ
4. Ⓐ Ⓑ Ⓒ Ⓓ
5. Ⓐ Ⓑ Ⓒ Ⓓ
6. Ⓐ Ⓑ Ⓒ Ⓓ
7. Ⓐ Ⓑ Ⓒ Ⓓ
8. Ⓐ Ⓑ Ⓒ Ⓓ

Sentence Structure: Practice # _____

Standard Usage: Practice # _____

1. Ⓐ Ⓑ Ⓒ Ⓓ
2. Ⓐ Ⓑ Ⓒ Ⓓ
3. Ⓐ Ⓑ Ⓒ Ⓓ
4. Ⓐ Ⓑ Ⓒ Ⓓ
5. Ⓐ Ⓑ Ⓒ Ⓓ
6. Ⓐ Ⓑ Ⓒ Ⓓ
7. Ⓐ Ⓑ Ⓒ Ⓓ
8. Ⓐ Ⓑ Ⓒ Ⓓ

Sentence Structure: Practice # _____

Standard Usage: Practice # _____

1. Ⓐ Ⓑ Ⓒ Ⓓ
2. Ⓐ Ⓑ Ⓒ Ⓓ
3. Ⓐ Ⓑ Ⓒ Ⓓ
4. Ⓐ Ⓑ Ⓒ Ⓓ
5. Ⓐ Ⓑ Ⓒ Ⓓ
6. Ⓐ Ⓑ Ⓒ Ⓓ
7. Ⓐ Ⓑ Ⓒ Ⓓ
8. Ⓐ Ⓑ Ⓒ Ⓓ

Sentence Structure: Practice # _____

Standard Usage: Practice # _____

1. Ⓐ Ⓑ Ⓒ Ⓓ
2. Ⓐ Ⓑ Ⓒ Ⓓ
3. Ⓐ Ⓑ Ⓒ Ⓓ
4. Ⓐ Ⓑ Ⓒ Ⓓ
5. Ⓐ Ⓑ Ⓒ Ⓓ
6. Ⓐ Ⓑ Ⓒ Ⓓ
7. Ⓐ Ⓑ Ⓒ Ⓓ
8. Ⓐ Ⓑ Ⓒ Ⓓ